The MRCGP Examination

A GUIDE FOR CANDIDATES AND TEACHERS

Fourth edition

Edited by
Richard Moore FRCGP

Published by
The Royal College of General Practitioners

The Royal College of General Practitioners was founded in 1952 with this object:
'To encourage, foster and maintain the highest possible standards in general practice and for that purpose to take or join with others in taking steps consistent with the charitable nature of that object which may assist towards the same.'
Among its responsibilities under its Royal Charter the College is entitled to:
'Diffuse information on all matters affecting general practice and issue such publications as may assist the object of the College.'

© Royal College of General Practitioners, 2000

First edition 1994
Second impression 1994
Third impression 1995

Second edition 1996

Third edition 1998

Fourth edition 2000

Published by
The Royal College of General Practitioners
14 Princes Gate, London SW7 1PU

Produced by Mulberry Media Services
Printed in Great Britain by College Hill Press, London.

ISBN 0 85084 255 7

Contents

Preface

New members of the College are always welcome, both because its members are its life-blood and should represent the great majority of the profession, and because the benefits the College offers affect the discipline of general practice as a whole. The assessment procedures for membership are therefore an essential part of the College's activity.

A major addition to the text in this edition is the inclusion of the College's new assessment procedure, membership by assessment of performance (MAP). Many GPs, who were previously not members but who have some years of experience in practice, would now like to join the College, but were understandably hesitant to sit an examination more suited to those still pursuing their vocational training. This new assessment procedure is now in place, and early suggestions are that it will prove very popular. The background and structure of MAP are only outlined in this book, but it is hoped that this outline offers a view of the process that will be informative and attractive to potential candidates.

The modular format of the MRCGP exam has been very successful and free from problems, although some minor adjustments have been made in the light of experience. The change has enhanced the reliability of the exam, the convenience for candidates and the effectiveness of the examiners. The new edition of this book takes account of these modifications, and introduces some additional examples and illustrations.

The contributions that the authors of this book have made are again gratefully acknowledged. Their willingness to give so much time and thought to writing their chapters, over and above their commitment to the examination, and to the development and introduction of MAP, is much appreciated.

An innovation for this edition is an epilogue written by Joanna Bircher, a recent candidate and winner of the Fraser Rose Medal in 1998. Her enthusiastic commitment to continuing education in new and exciting ways is an excellent example to all general practitioners, which should be widely followed.

The modular format allows both distinction and merit grades. Such incentives are provided as an encouragement to all candidates in the MRCGP, and the educational opportunities of MAP will have a similarly stimulating effect. In the fullness of time these procedures will surely bear fruit in the continuing improvement of standards in the profession of general practice.

Note

Every effort has been made to ensure that information given in the text is accurate at the time of going to press. However, because the MRCGP examination is under constant review, changes are made from time to time which may not be reflected in this book. Potential candidates are therefore advised to obtain up-to-date information from the examination department of the Royal College of General Practitioners when planning their applications.

Preface to third edition

The changes referred to in the prefaces to previous editions of this book, which follow (see pp viii-xix), continue apace and have necessitated a new edition in less than two years. In that time I have retired from the panel of examiners, though I retain an abiding interest in the MRCGP, and therefore am no longer in a position to write as a sole author. I am therefore more than grateful to my friends and colleagues as examiners who have written chapters for this new edition. They all hold significant positions in the panel as chairman or members of the Examination Board, or as convenors, as well as having wide experience of teaching and assessment in other appointments. Their authoritative contributions will add immensely to the value of the book for its readers, and the additional work and dedication to the examination which this has involved should be formally and very gratefully acknowledged.

November 1997   RICHARD MOORE

Preface to second edition

Since the first edition of this book was published in March 1993 there have been substantial changes both in the examination for membership of the Royal College of General Practitioners and in the procedure for demonstrating the satisfactory completion of training for general practice.

In the recent past most, but not all, doctors coming to the end of their training chose to take the MRCGP examination to show that they had indeed reached an adequate standard, and thereby eligible to become members of the College. With the introduction of compulsory summative assessment all doctors wishing to become principals in practice in the NHS must take a test which contains some elements similar to the MRCGP examination, namely a multiple-choice question paper (MCQ) to assess knowledge and a videotape to assess consultation skills. They must also complete a project of written work and have an adequate report from their trainer.

How this will relate to the MRCGP examination in the view of new entrants to the profession remains to be seen, but it is expected that many will see the examination as a test which requires a higher standard than the basic adequacy expected in the United Kingdom regional advisers' summative assessment system. For the last 20 years or so a very large proportion of doctors completing their training have risen to the challenge of the MRCGP examination, which is greatly to their credit, and it is likely that this will be so in future as new doctors see the benefits of demonstrating their competence and achievement in this way.

At the same time there have been significant changes in the MRCGP examination itself, which are quite independent of the summative assessment requirements but, as is now becoming clear, are complementary to them. Two changes are of major significance, namely the division of the examination into two sections, which may be taken together or at separate times, and the introduction of the consulting skills component.

The first section, part A, consists of an MCQ to test knowledge and problem-solving skills, and an assessment of consulting skills by examination of videotaped consultations, or if that is not possible by the simulated surgery system. The MCQ can be taken on four occasions in the year, and the videotape may be submitted at the time of taking the MCQ. A satisfactory mark in the MCQ will exempt that candidate from the UK regional advisers' MCQ, and the same videotape may be used for both the MRCGP and the summative assessment procedure. Part B consists of the other written papers as before, the modified essay question and the critical reading question (CRQ) papers, and the two oral examinations if the marks of the written papers are adequate. Another important change is the introduction of a minimum mark in all sections of the examination, so that a candidate falling below this mark in one or more sections will not pass the examination overall whatever the total marks.*

Other changes have occurred in the course of the natural evolution of the examination, such as a new form to the practice experience questionnaire (PEQ) making it more relevant to the candidates who are now almost entirely doctors completing their training. The papers and the orals have also developed in a variety of ways, though less radically.

I have again been assisted in the revision of the text by many people whose help has been invaluable. Declan Dwyer and Roger Neighbour have supplied further examples of CRQ and MEQ questions with comments, and Peter Tate and Liz Bingham have advised on their parts of the consulting skills component which has been undergoing rapid evolution as its introduction approaches.

A new contributor to this support is Peter Elliott who has provided new examples of questions for the MCQ, and his skill and ingenuity in doing this is much appreciated. John Foulkes, now head of the examination department has advised about the changes to the marking system, and he and his staff in the department have been more than helpful in answering enquiries and supplying material. All this help is gratefully acknowledged. Indeed the new edition of the text would have been impossible without this generous help.

All these changes are described in the new edition of this book, and should be studied carefully for they are important for candidates and teachers alike. It is to be hoped that the way in which they are described will encourage and inspire the reader, whether he or she be a candidate, a teacher or an interested observer. There is no doubt that the examination is thriving as it faces the new demands of a complex and developing discipline, and the panel of examiners and the examination department are as enthusiastic and dedicated as ever.

The new generation of general practitioner registrars should be encouraged to rise to the challenge of the MRCGP examination as their predecessors did, and show their commitment to the profession despite the problems that beset it. Not only would they be wise to sit the membership examination, but having passed it should become and remain active subscribers, for the College exists not just as an examining body, but as the principal organization in the country dedicated to setting and promoting the highest standards in primary care.

This second edition, like the first, is therefore dedicated to all those past and future candidates of the MRCGP examination who have made and will make the Royal College of General Practitioners the success that it is and deserves to remain.

November 1995   RICHARD MOORE

The revisions to rules described in this paragraph have been superceded by the changes to modular format described in later chapters.

Editor's preface to second edition

The history of the development of the MRCGP examination, set against the history of the development of the College itself, has already been described in a College publication — *Occasional Paper 46* (RCGP, 1990) but this is the first time the College has published a book of practical help to candidates.

The big question which has never been fully answered is: Why take the examination? There are in fact five reasons why general practitioners should take the MRCGP examination, which is still a voluntary choice in this country, and the reasons need to be clearly understood.

1 Personal satisfaction

The General Medical Council is the governing body of the whole of the medical profession and it recognises only one British 'additional registrable qualification' in general medical practice — the MRCGP. There is no other way in which a doctor who has chosen to be a general practitioner in the UK can obtain a higher qualification in his or her subject other than by passing this examination. The examination has been rigorously developed since 1965 (RCGP, 1990) and has been subjected to the most severe critical analysis in its methods and techniques. *The Lancet* (1990) has commented that among the royal colleges the Royal College of General Practitioners comes out well in the degree of openness with which it approaches its examination and the rationale for the way it is constructed.

It follows, therefore, that there is considerable professional pride for young doctors who, having completed vocational training for general practice, obtain the seal of approval from their Royal College that they have reached an appropriate standard to be an unsupervised principal in general practice.

It is not only a matter of pride for registrars but also for trainers, course organizers and regional advisers, who play an important part in the individual and collective performance of registrars. Some training practices have an outstanding record in the MRCGP examination, with 100% or near 100% achievement of their registrars, and this often reflects high-quality teaching in the practice and sustained educational support given throughout the general practice year.

2 Career advancement

The examination also helps doctors to further their career in general practice. It has been known for many years that the MRCGP is effectively compulsory for those who aspire to hold leading positions in general practice; for example, all the professors of general practice and regional advisers are College members, as are nearly all the associate advisers and the great majority of course organizers. In some regions the MRCGP is required for those who wish to become trainers. Some university departments of general practice will only appoint research fellows who have satisfied the examiners of the College as to their clinical competence.

However, doctors holding these positions form a relative minority among general practitioners, who number 30,000 in the UK. The real issue in terms of career advancement is whether or not the MRCGP will be required for appointment as a principal in general practice, and this policy is moving up the national agenda swiftly at the time of writing.

First, it is important to remember that in every other branch of medical practice doctors are individually assessed by the appropriate royal college or faculty on their chosen subject. In the past, such assessment was effectively required before appointment as a consultant and the royal colleges have assessors on consultant appointment selection committees. However, now most of the royal colleges and specialist faculties require possession of the appropriate royal college diploma before entry for training. Thus, for example, the MRCP is effectively required before a doctor can enrol as a registrar of medicine and the FRCS (now MRCS) is required for entry to training programmes in surgery.

Against this background it becomes increasingly anomalous that in the largest branch of the profession doctors should not be systematically examined by their own royal college, particularly at the end of a period of training which alone is statutory and governed by act of Parliament.

It was in 1979 that a key profile policy was developed by the last royal commission to examine the National Health Service in Britain. The crucial paragraph 7.29 reads:

'...but, as in other specialities, experience in itself will not be a sufficient indication of quality of performance — it will need to be tested and competence demonstrated. As with hospital specialities possession of the postgraduate qualification of the relevant royal college should become the norm for appointment as a principal in general practice [in the NHS].'

This paragraph attracted relatively little attention at the time. However, it was finally examined by the Royal College of General Practitioners in May 1993 when its Council formally adopted this policy. Thus it is now the policy of the College that in future all those who are to hold unsupervised responsibility as principals in general practice in the National Health Service should hold the MRCGP.

The College does not of itself have the power to introduce this ruling. Ultimately either family health services authorities or the Department of Health will need to adopt the policy. However, previous College policies of this kind have been followed by implementation usually within about 12 years: for example, College policy urging the introduction of vocational training (CGP, 1965) was implemented by act of Parliament in 1977, and its policy on the care of children (RCGP, 1978) was implemented in the 1990 General Practitioner Contract. It must therefore be assumed that sooner or later this examination will be required for entry as a principal and the question now is not whether but when.

In fact, implementation of this new policy may well come much faster than expected. For years many practices have quietly insisted that only members will be shortlisted for partnerships, and a growing number of family health services authorities are now doing the same for single-handed vacancies. To this extent the profession has great power in its own hands since most partnerships are filled by practices themselves.

3 Quality marker

As if these professional pressures were not enough, other developments in society are also focusing attention on possession of the MRCGP as a marker of quality. The decision by the General Medical Council to erase from the register a young doctor who held the JCPTGP certificate but whose diabetic patient died has led to serious questions about the degree of guarantee that the JCPTGP certificate (unsupported by an MRCGP) offers patients, and in a television programme in October 1993 comment was made on the performance of a few unfortunate general practitioners who, it was alleged, had made clinical errors, as to whether or not they possessed the MRCGP. This led to patients ringing the College to find out how they could identify whether or not their own family doctor held this qualification.

Early in the College's history, a famous leader of the College, Fraser Rose said that people were joining the College at that time 'not because we are better doctors, but because we wish to become better doctors'. This marvellous phrase has rung through the ages but now, in the 1990s, it may be starting to become out of date.

Evidence is steadily accumulating that general practitioners who are members of the College differ from those who are not. In 1967, Cartwright found that members were better equipped, offered a wider range of services and had a deeper understanding of the psychiatric aspects of general practice. More recently, it has been found that members are significantly less likely to be reprimanded or erased by the General Medical Council or to be found in breach of their terms of service by the National Health Service (DoH, 1988; personal communication).

If these early reports stand the test of time, the MRCGP may come increasingly to be seen as a quality marker, a badge signalling to patients a higher likelihood of competence — although of course this will never mean that there are not some outstandingly good general practitioners who are not members of the College.

4 Fellowship by Assessment

A new reason for joining the College as a member emerged in 1989, when the College introduced a new form of Fellowship based on the quality of care provided for patients in general practice. This was done with the deliberate intent of producing a gold standard of clinical care in British general practice.

The unique features of this are that the criteria are research (evidence) based, they are published in advance, they are known to patients and doctors, and the assessment process is carried out in the doctor's practice by peers (three Fellows of the College). The standards are reviewed annually to take into account advances in research and clinical practice.

The standards were deliberately set very high right from the start, so that fellowship by assessment would be an achievement of which all doctors could be proud. By November 1995, 70 general practitioners had achieved this and were working in practices caring for about half a million patients.

The rate of increase in numbers is considerable and there are now groups of general practitioners working for fellowship by assessment in many different parts of the United Kingdom. It is certain to grow and in some parts of the country it is being actively encouraged by the National Health Service. For example, in Devon the FHSA/Health Authority there pays £1000 to any general practitioner who confirms in writing that he or she is a serious candidate.

By its constitution, Fellowship is a higher grade of membership of the College and it is only possible for members to take it. Those who ultimately aspire to the highest clinical standards, and wish to demonstrate them in this way need therefore to join the College as a member first. Richard Moore writes further on fellowship by assessment in chapter 15.

5 Financial advantage

The actual cost of becoming a member of the College is a tax allowable expense which may be channelled either through the practice account (preferable if all partners are members) or personally, but in either event it will attract tax relief for the doctor at their highest rate (25% or 40% in February 1996).

Since 1991 College members have also been able to save costs by joining a new professional indemnity service offered by the Medical Insurance Agency (*General Practitioner*, 1991). The insurance premium for MRCGPs is now less than for non-MRCGPs with a difference greater than the annual cost of the College's subscription, so that payment of the annual indemnity premium means that for a growing number of College members their whole annual subscription to the College (£244 pa in 1996) is effectively free.

If claims against doctors continue to rise and if College members' premiums continue to justify a differential, possessing the MRCGP could become increasingly financially advantageous.

6 Supporting the discipline

The final reason for being a member of the College is simply that it is part of the collective, professional responsibility of general practitioners to support the only royal college they have in their subject. Whereas there are often multiple specialist Colleges for one discipline, for example, there is a Royal College of Physicians of Edinburgh, Glasgow and London, there is for general practitioners in the United Kingdom only one national academic body which can represent their interests.

The College is a voluntary body and, as its accounts reveal, it is heavily dependent on subscriptions for its income (RCGP, 1993). About three-quarters of all the working money in the College depends on the subscriptions of members and without these general practitioners would be substantially less well represented. College subscriptions support about 100 general practitioners who represent general practice on a whole variety of other organizations.

The voice of general practice has always been dangerously thin on the ground and is still seriously stretched — often the College representative is the only general practitioner in the room. Some highly prestigious organizations, notably the Conference of Medical Royal Colleges and Faculties in the United Kingdom, are such that the General Medical Services Committee could never aspire to attend, so that the whole thrust of representation of general practice depends on the College member appointed by the Council to speak for all of us.

This network of representation, which operates both nationally and locally, forms an important bulwark in preventing hostile policies and arrangements being thrust on general practice. There can be no doubt that membership of the College plays an important role in making sure the voice of general practice is heard in every arena.

The effectiveness of the College as a stimulus for change and development is already well proved. It was the College that devised and developed the first scientific journal of general practice in the world which today ranks in the first 20 among the medical journals in the USA citation index (ISI, 1993); it was the College whose work led to the introduction of the Vocational Training Act; and it was the College that devised and developed the first registrable postgraduate qualification in general practice — the MRCGP examination. All of this had to be done by general practitioners for general practitioners.

Nor should it be forgotten that the College offers support to the individual not just the discipline as a whole. One of the great strengths of the College is that there is a regional organization and there is a faculty of the College in every part of the United Kingdom, and an overseas faculty as well. The faculties run local meetings, lectures and varying special interest groups for members, offering support in a way that could not be done centrally.

Conclusion

Although some of these issues have yet to be finally clarified, it can be seen that there are powerful reasons why young doctors should take the examination, and that the best advice that anyone can now give to a younger colleague pursuing a career in general practice is to take the examination and remain associated with the College thereafter.

This book is the third in a series of practical workbooks published by the College, and anyone wishing to become a member of the College by examination will find it an invaluable source of information. Written by an experienced College examiner, the book should make its own valuable contribution to the development not only of the examination but of the College itself.

January 1996

Denis Pereira Gray
Honorary Editor
College Publications

References

Cartwright A (1967) *Patients and their Doctors*. London, Routledge and Kegan Paul.

College of General Practitioners (1965) *Special Vocational Training for General Practice*. Report from General Practice 1. London CGP

General Practitioner (1991) 6 April.

The Lancet (1990) Examining the Royal Colleges' examinations. Editorial, 355, 443.

Royal College of General Practitioners (1978) The care of children. *Journal of the Royal College of General Practitioners* 28, 553-556.

Royal College of General Practitioners (1990) *Examination for Membership of the Royal College of General Practitioners (MRCGP)* Occasional Paper 46. Ed. Lockie C. London, RCGP.

Royal College of General Practitioners (1995) Honorary Treasurer's Report. In *RCGP Member's Reference Book*. London, Sterling.

Royal Commission on the National Health Service (1979) *Report.* para 7.29. London, HMSO.

Institute for Scientific Information (1993) IV. *Subject category listing: Journals ranked by impact factor within category.* Philadelphia, USA: ISI

Note

Since this preface was written, the GMC has changed its procedures so that there are no longer any additional registrable qualifications. Also the entry requirement for surgical training is now the MRCS.

1   The origin and development of the examination

Richard Moore

Prologue

The combination of knowledge and caring, of science and understanding, underlie the profession of general practice as it is today. This is no new idea, for the concept of education and assessment in this discipline goes back to the early 19th century, when for the first time regulation and registration of medical practitioners were being debated and introduced. Plans to found a 'College of General Practitioners' were put forward in the 1840s but did not find universal approval.

An early proponent was William Gaitskell, the president of the Metropolitan Society of General Practitioners in Medicine and Surgery, who wrote to *The Lancet* in 1830 saying: 'Various branches of the medical profession have colleges, charters and corporations, from which the general practitioner is either altogether excluded, or attached as an appendage only; he is not admitted to a participation in their councils, or to share in their honours; as a general practitioner, he belongs to no one branch, and is, therefore, virtually excluded from all.' (*The Practitioner* 1953a.)

A few years later in 1844, Dr James Cole, of Bewdley in Worcestershire, writing in *The Provincial Medical and Surgical Journal*, proposed a remedy for the educational subservience of his part of the medical profession. This was the 'incorporation of the eighteen thousand Licentiates of the Hall [of Apothecaries] into a Royal College of Apothecaries... By this means we obtain... a clearly defined, well and thoroughly educated body of Medical Practitioners who shall be in every way worthy of the respect of their colleagues and of public confidence.' In the same year correspondence in *The*

Lancet was lively, with proposals for the foundation of a 'royal college of general practitioners in medicine, surgery and midwifery', and of 'The College of Medicine and Surgery'. Calls from all over the country supported the idea, especially after the Royal College of Surgeons was granted a new charter disenfranchising general practitioner members. Dr George Ross of Kennington, wrote in *The Lancet* in 1844: 'The laws of the College of Surgeons are made for the Council and Fellows. Let them retain their privileges and retain the honours of their institution; but let the general practitioner have also his college — he has interests to support and a respectability to uphold; let him therefore possess the means of accomplishing these things.' (*The Practitioner* 1953a.)

The British Medical Association supported the proposals, saying that it was 'imperatively necessary' to form a 'legal union of the general practitioners in this kingdom into a distinct corporation', and this indeed did happen with the formation of a National Association of General Practitioners in Medicine, Surgery, and Midwifery. The purpose of this was to petition for a charter of incorporation, and might well have succeeded but for its rather ineffective organisation. Parliament was debating medical reform, and proposals for a college of general practitioners were included in a series of bills before Parliament. Unfortunately, confusion surrounded the whole movement; support was vociferous from London but less so from the provinces, and the voice of the College of Surgeons, reluctant to yield its educational power, prevailed over the pleas of a disorganised and divided profession. The proposals foundered.

The College is founded

One hundred years later there was a crisis among general practitioners who experienced serious loss of incomes after the introduction of the National Health Service in 1948 and the public's expectation of free treatment, and were overwhelmed by work but starved of resources.

The determination of a small but dedicated group of doctors rekindled the enthusiasm of the profession to take responsibility for its own education and development. It had lacked control of its own destiny for too long 'without headquarters, without academic leadership of its own, without much influence over undergraduate or postgraduate teaching, and without the status of their specialist colleagues'. (Fry, Hunt and Pinsent, 1982.)

The far-sighted efforts of John Hunt, Fraser Rose and others, unfamiliar with the failures of a hundred years before, encountered opposition from their specialist colleagues as forceful as that which faced their predecessors. Their determination bore fruit, however, in 1953 with the foundation The College of General Practitioners, which in 1967 became a Royal College by command of Her Majesty Queen Elizabeth II. Dr Fraser Rose was the first chairman of the Board of Censors responsible for devising and introducing the examination, and is commemorated by the Fraser Rose Medal awarded to the candidate who gains the highest mark in the examinations each year.

The purpose of membership

The objectives of the College are: 'To encourage, foster and maintain the highest possible standards in general practice, and for that purpose to take any steps which may assist towards the same.' Its charter also permits it to grant diplomas and certificates of proficiency in general medical practice (RCGP 1999). An important step in meeting these obligations was the introduction of the membership examination in 1965, whose purpose was, and remains, to determine whether applicants for membership have reached the standard of competence expected of members of the College. When mandatory training for general practice was introduced the regulations governing it did not specify a nationally standardised end-point assessment, so many doctors began to take the MRCGP examination to demonstrate to themselves and others that they had completed their training satisfactorily.

The majority of candidates are now doctors completing their vocational training, who see it as a means of motivating their studies and demonstrating their abilities to prospective partners as well as a way of entering the College. There are still some candidates who are already in practice as principals, for example prospective trainers, but the introduction of membership by assessment of performance (MAP) is likely to become a more attractive route of entry for those who have been principals for five years or more. An outline of MAP and its process is given in chapters 10 and 11.

The College now has more than 15,000 Fellows and members, and supports a wide range of educational and other activities. These include the promotion of vocational training, continuing education, courses in clinical and management skills, research, international contacts and social events. Not least among its activities is a wide range of publications, 78 occasional papers, reports from practice, and books and other materials on clinical and management topics. The College's journal, *The British Journal of General Practice,* is the highest-rated journal about general practice in the world in terms of its impact factor (RCGP, 1997).

Although the College's headquarters are in London, it also has Scottish and Welsh Councils and 32 faculties representing its membership locally. It is by no means only a central administrative organisation, but a society in which active participation of all its members at a local, regional or national level is welcome and encouraged. There are also many overseas members.

Although not an official negotiating body in the context of terms and conditions of work in the National Health Service, the RCGP has important contacts with other medical royal colleges, universities, and with government and NHS administration. Membership of the College enables general practitioners to have the benefits of a professional organisation specific to their own discipline, and a voice in developing and managing the medical profession as a whole.

The faculty structure is designed to encourage all members to participate in College activities locally and to make representations to Council and its officers, avoiding the concentration of thought and opinion-forming by a headquarters elite. To fulfil its obligation to 'promote and maintain the highest possible standards', the College needs its members not just to pass its membership procedures but to remain members and contribute to its activities.

The candidates

Before the examination became compulsory for membership of the College in 1968, there were various ways in which aspiring members could qualify for it. They were based on relevant experience and included either the possession of a higher postgraduate degree or diploma, or the promise to accept 'postgraduate instruction for three days each year or an equivalent number of hours' (*The Practitioner*, 1953b). With the hindsight of half a century the word instruction rather than education, and the idea that possession of a diploma removes the need for a promise about continuing education seem strangely anachronistic.

From the time of its foundation the College always intended to institute an examination, and the first took place in 1965, 13 years later. There were five candidates, all of whom were successful. By the 1970s, the examination had become recognized as the natural way to demonstrate satisfactory completion of education for general practice, and for the last 20 years there have been up to 2000 candidates every year. In 1996, they exceeded 2000, a record 1397 sitting the summer exam. During this time about three-quarters of the candidates were successful.

A review of candidates' reasons for taking the examination (Tombleson and Wakeford, 1989) showed that of 280 trainees who answered a questionnaire, 71% saw the examination as a help in getting a job and 67% as a personal hurdle or discipline. Furthermore, 66% considered that its most important role was to ensure a basic level of competence before supervision ceased. Some respondents believed that at some time in the future membership of the RCGP would become necessary for entry to general practice. Although many people now argue that MRCGP should be the norm for principals it is not yet an essential requirement.

The examiners

The Panel of Examiners takes its authority from the Council of the College through the Examination Board, the chairman of which is a member of Council and is usually an examiner. The panel has about

150 members who are all members or Fellows of the College, and have been proposed as examiners through the faculty structure. Members interested in teaching and assessment may be invited by their faculty board officers to consider becoming examiners, and anyone interested in joining the panel may volunteer with the support of appropriate references. Many, but not all, have a special interest in continuing medical education as trainers, tutors, course organizers or directors of postgraduate education, and some are in academic posts. Prospective new examiners must have passed the examination themselves and, if that was not recently, take the papers again. The initial assessment of potential examiners consists of two days observing the examinations and an assessment day involving group work, mock oral examination and learning about the examination and its processes. Not all who are proposed are appointed, and some choose not to accept the appointment if offered.

All examiners continue their training throughout their time on the panel. This consists of regular periods observing oral examinations and participating in subsequent critical discussions, feedback on the marking performance, and video recording and analysis of the oral examinations they have taken. Discussion of techniques, policies and developments takes place at the annual three-day workshop.

The scope of the MRCGP

The agenda for education of general practitioners was set out in the College's publication, *The Future General Practitioner — Learning and Teaching* (RCGP, 1972). This fundamental report laid the foundations of a programme for education for general practice. It referred to a general practitioner as 'a doctor who provides personal primary and continuing care to individuals and families' and whose 'diagnoses are composed in physical, psychological and social terms'. Such doctors 'work in a team and delegate when necessary' and 'intervene educationally, preventively and therapeutically to promote...health'

That defined the nature of general practice in Great Britain and formed the basis on which the examination has been offered to candidates for the past 25 years. Since then the examination has evolved from its simple conventional 'essays-plus-viva-voce' format into its present complex and efficient organization, taking account of both the enormous developments in the scope and effectiveness of primary care, and developments in educational assessment techniques. Whatever criticisms may be made of the need for or methods of the exam it cannot be argued that it has stood still.

The outstanding achievement of the College in its early years was a widespread acceptance of the belief that general practice is a medical discipline in its own right, requiring basic and continuing education, self-esteem among its practitioners, and recognition and respect from colleagues in other disciplines. In doing so it has realised the aspirations of our predecessors of 150 years ago.

The discipline of general practice is very wide, and embraces aspects of many others. Therefore the examination covers the whole range of activities in general medical practice in the United Kingdom, including areas which overlap with other disciplines and professions. This is important, for the MRCGP is not merely a test of clinical knowledge or diagnostic skill, but also an assessment of candidates' abilities in consulting and communication skills, in practice management, and of their understanding of areas such as ethics and medical politics. It does not dictate a syllabus, but reflects the current ideas of good practice which are set out in its blueprint, as described in chapter 3. It seeks to determine whether candidates have a rational basis for the beliefs they hold and the actions they propose sufficient to enable them to achieve the standards of competence demanded of members of a professional college.

An evolving programme

From the general public's point of view, examinations may be seen as a guarantee of quality, though in the past it has been noted that most of the royal colleges did not provide enough information about their examinations for that judgement to be made (*The Lancet*, 1990). However, the RCGP was seen as an 'honourable exception' by *The Lancet* because it is at pains to publish enough information to enable interested parties to judge the adequacy of its membership examination. The *British Medical Journal* published a series of articles describing the examinations of the royal colleges, and commented favourably on the MRCGP examination and the College's confidence in accepting such outside scrutiny (Godlee, 1991).

However good an examination is, it must not be complacent, for improvement is always possible. There had been many developments in the early years, but by the 1980s the need to offer the increasingly numerous candidates a reliable and acceptable examination brought about a major review. This was carried out in 1986-87 by Dr David Swanson (Swanson 1987), an American psychometrician, who commended the system as it then was, but advised changes in some areas to make it more reliable.

The challenge was taken up, and under the guidance of the Centre for Medical Education of the University of Dundee, several developments were started. One of the principal needs was to improve the examination's reliability; that is to say that to ensure that if a candidate were to take the same examination again the result would also be the same. Reliability is measured by a statistical formula known as alpha coefficient, where 1.0 is ideal though not attainable in practice, and 0.8 or more is acceptable. To achieve this the old essay style questions were abandoned in favour of the specially devised critical reading questions (CRQ), which were more discriminating and relevant.

The practice experience questionnaire (PEQ), which generated considerable work for candidates but was often little used in the examination was abandoned. It had been designed to test clinical competence, but had to do so indirectly because the large number of candidates created problems of logistics, consistency and reliability. This was undoubtedly a weakness, which has been resolved by the introduction of the consulting skills module in which candidates submit videotapes of actual consultations, or, if that is impracticable, have their competence assessed in a simulated surgery. This is proving to be a very reliable way to test the application of skills and knowledge in practice, and is a step in the direction of the assessment of performance rather than competence.

In 1998 further developments were introduced in response to the new summative assessment procedures that all registrars must undergo on the completion of their training. These changes include:-

- The amalgamation of CRQ and the modified essay question (MCQ) into Paper 1
- The addition of machine markable elements of CRQ to the MCQ to form Paper 2 to test the ability to apply knowledge rather than merely possess it
- Revision of the orals to make them shorter but more reliable

These changes further improved the reliability of the examination, which has been shown to be consistently reliable throughout.

This regular review of its methods and relevance to the needs of its candidates and others has changed the form of the examination, and the content has also kept pace with the developments in practice. The change to a modular form, which seemed so radical when it was introduced, has become accepted within a short time, and can be seen as a further stage in the continuous development of the MRCGP examination.

Future challenges

Medicine as a whole and primary care in particular change and develop as new ideas and techniques are introduced, sometimes very rapidly. The RCGP has reviewed the impact of such changes in its *Report from General Practice 27; The Nature of General Medical Practice* (RCGP, 1996). While the essential content of the general practitioner's work has not altered, namely the personal, continuing and primary care in which doctor and patient have a long-term and close relationship, there are also substantial additional responsibilities.

The Nature of General Practice describes a 'generalist care team' with responsibilities in doctoring, nursing and managing, and a 'referral network' with 14 or more specialist agencies such as counsellors, dieticians, health visitors and psychiatric nurses; this is a big extension of 'working in a team and delegating when necessary', mentioned in *The Future General Practitioner.* Similarly, there are big changes in both clinical and managerial activities. Enormous developments in pharmacology, emergency medicine, the care of the chronically or terminally ill, ethical issues, medico-legal matters and a big increase in complaints and litigation, mean that general practice encompasses a far greater range of skills and responsibilities than it did even in 1972.

The size of many practices is now such that management and administrative skills of high order are required to ensure effective and efficient application of the resources they control. Furthermore, the great success of education for general practice and the increasing expectation of the public that its doctors should be competent and accountable has very properly prompted the demand that all new entrants to the profession should be required to demonstrate their competence, as opposed to merely having it certified by those who have trained them.

The MRCGP has evolved over the half-century since it was first conceived to meet these needs. Success in it is recognised as a demonstration of a candidate's ability to make a competent beginning in his or her career. But it is only a beginning, for the desirability and acceptance of continuing medical education, the developments in evidence-based practice and, in the near future, revalidation mean that more such challenges will occur throughout that career.

The new member of the College will need to seize the many other opportunities for education and professional development that the Royal College of General Practitioners now offers.

References

Fry J, Hunt JH and Pinsent RJFH (1982) *A History of the Royal College of General Practitioners. The first 25 years.* Lancaster, MTP Press.

Godlee F (1991) MRCGP: Examining the exam. *British Medical Journal* 303, 235-238.

The Lancet (1990) Examining the Royal Colleges' examinations. Editorial 335, 443

The Practitioner (1953a) Report of Foundation Council of the College of General Practitioners 170, Supplement 1-32.

The Practitioner (1953b) College of General Practitioners Editorial 170, 1-2.

Royal College of General Practitioners (1972) *The Future General Practitioner, Learning and Teaching*. London, British Medical Journal.

RCGP (1996) *Report form General Practice 27; the Nature of General Medical Practice*. London, The Royal College of General Practitioners.

RCGP (1999) *RCGP Annual Report: Members Reference Book 1999/2000*, p 4. London, Campden Publishing Ltd.

RCGP (1997b) *RCGP Annual Report: Members Reference Book 1997*. London, Campden Publishing Ltd.

Swanson DB, (1987) *Review of Membership Examination Procedures of the Royal College of General Practitioners*. Unpublished.

Tombleson P and Wakeford R (1989) Why do Trainees take the Membership examination? *Journal of the Royal College of General Practitioners* 39, 168-171.

2   Why does the examination keep changing?

David Haslam

The MRCGP will never be the same again. But then, it probably never was. As the first chapter of this book has shown, ever since the first five candidates took the MRCGP examination in 1965, it has undergone a life of perpetual change. Indeed, while many medical examinations have stagnated or drifted, the MRCGP has been constantly under revision (Walker 1990).

Change in any aspect of life can be exciting, and it can be threatening. As every family doctor is only too well aware, the speciality of general practice has changed out of all recognition in the UK over the past few years. We have seen the introduction of computers, the extended use of the team, rationing, fundholding, commissioning, and now primary care groups, not to mention the increased use of audit, evidence-based medicine, and so on and on through a near endless list. It would therefore be absurd and anachronistic if the specialty's flagship examination should not have done the same. And, in the same way that the core values of general practice have remained unchanged, so has the core of the examination remained focused on high-quality patient care.

Since I became an examiner over 15 years ago, changes to the examination have included the introduction of the critical reading paper (CRQ), restructuring of the modified essay question (MEQ) to more fairly represent everyday practice, refinement of the oral examinations with greater emphasis on examiner training (Wakeford, Southgate and Wass 1995), and the introduction of the consulting skills assessment (by video or simulated surgery) (Bingham et al 1996). Indeed this constant refinement of both techniques and examiner training results in other medical royal colleges frequently turning to the MRCGP for advice. It seems likely that in assessment, as well as in education, general practice is the leading medical speciality in the United Kingdom. If such a lead is to be maintained, however, what direction should it take?

Summative assessment introduced

The arrival of summative assessment was the trigger for the recent radical changes. I hope that readers will tolerate a brief historical review of the introduction of this assessment, as it is fundamental to an understanding of what happened to the MRCGP examination. Summative assessment was introduced in the UK as a professionally led assessment of all new entrants to general practice. (JCPT, 1993; Hayden, 1996). Using a number of assessment techniques, it was designed to ensure that GP registrars reach a minimum standard before being permitted to practise unsupervised. It was difficult to disagree with the basic concept. I remember discussing this with non-medical friends and they were astonished, not to say horrified, that it was then possible to become a GP without any formal check, other than a report by your trainer, that your knowledge and skills were appropriate .

However, this caused a problem for the RCGP. The College had long held the view that the MRCGP qualification should be held by all who become a principal in general practice. The word 'should' was all important. Should is not must. There was never any belief that the holding of this qualification ought to be mandatory, and there would be no way of enforcing this. After all, not all GPs are members of the College, and some are actively hostile. In addition, as the College believed that all principals should hold the whole qualification, it would be illogical to allow bits of the examination to be used as part of a lower level assessment. While at times this argument resembled debates about how many angels could dance on the head of a pin, it was nevertheless of vital importance.

The crux of the problem was that the MRCGP is set at an optimum, rather than a minimum, standard whereas the compulsory summative assessment was to be at a minimum level — an attempt to ensure that the really poor doctor would be prevented from practising without further training. While a significant proportion of the training and medico-political establishment felt that it was entirely logical to use the MRCGP examination — in the same way that other royal colleges expect membership of anyone who wishes to practise in their specialty — there was sufficient resistance to make this impossible.

Options for progress

So, what were the options? There appeared to be three main possibilities:

a) Every intending GP should take the MRCGP
b) Parts of the MRCGP (such as the MCQ) would be used as a lower level assessment
c) There should be an alternative, minimal level, assessment which all intending GPs should take.

The first option was entirely unacceptable to a number of registrars and medical politicians, even though 85% of all registrars already took the examination. The second was unacceptable to the Council of the RCGP, on the entirely logical grounds that they had already stated that all intending GPs should hold the entire examination. The last would result in most registrars having to take two separate assessments.

While many thought the duplication inherent in the third option was absurd, it was also claimed that there was insufficient academic evidence to allow those who passed the MRCGP to be exempt from summative assessment. However, it was agreed that doctors who wished to take alternative assessment methods could apply to the Joint Committee on Postgraduate Training in General Practice (JCPTGP) to have their methods accepted as an exemption to part of the summative assessment tests.

The summative assessment tests consist of an MCQ, a trainer's report, a piece of written work, and a video assessment of consulting skills. The RCGP applied for exemption from the summative assessment MCQ for those who had reached a suitable standard in the MRCGP MCQ. This was granted. As the summative assessment MCQ was available four times a year, it was believed that it would be extremely friendly and helpful to candidates if the MRCGP MCQ was also to be made available four times a year. Council agreed to this, and that it could be taken at a different time to the other written papers, and that up to two re-sits could be taken.

Problems with the structure of the MRCGP

It became apparent that allowing the MCQ to be taken out of phase with the other parts had completely destroyed the fundamental structure of the examination. A number of problems resulted:

• Because the CRQ and MEQ had been disconnected from the MCQ, they had to stand alone.

• To preserve their psychometric reliability they would have to be increased in length. This meant that all three written papers could no longer be taken on a single day; the CRQ and MEQ together involve six hours of writing prose.

• In the past, all examination statistics had been based on a single cohort of candidates who took the examination at the same time. It was also simple to calculate the top 85% who would be called to oral. By allowing the papers to be taken at different times a new system of grading was required to allow the results to stand alone. The new system awards each paper a mark from A (highest) to F (lowest). A, B and C are passing grades, and candidates need to achieve C overall to pass; thus candidates who achieve D in one paper can offset an A or a B in another paper and be 'pulled up' to an overall C level and so pass. E and F are failing grades.

• Candidates began to change their behaviour. Because they knew their grades from each written paper, they were able to calculate what grade they would need in the oral to pass overall. Some decided that they would have a better chance of passing the oral if they improved their written grades, and chose to retake the MCQ in the hope of doing so.

• It became increasingly obvious that it was unfair to allow candidates who failed the MCQ or consulting skills assessment to retake these sections of the examination for a nominal fee, but to insist that candidates who failed any other section of the examination should pay the full fee and retake the entire examination. This appeared both academically and financially unfair.

In summary, many candidates and many examiners felt that the whole examination structure had become unnecessarily complex. It was clearly necessary to have a radical re-think. For at least 10 years, modularisation had been discussed within the examination as a logical way forward. The separation of the MCQ from the rest of the examination was a first step down the road of modularisation, and the changes that followed were a logical result of this first step.

Rationalising the examination

The examination board believed that the changed situation had revealed a number of opportunities for streamlining and rationalising the MRCGP examination, and in June 1997 its proposals were considered and enthusiastically approved by the Council of the Royal College of General Practitioners. These proposals took as their starting point a number of important principles:

• The examination should combine sound academic credentials with candidate friendliness

• The highest possible validity and reliability should be maintained. Naturally, without these, any move towards extending the role of the exam would be hard to justify

• The examination should remain as fair a test as possible

• The examination should retain overall, though not necessarily specific, congruence with the requirements of summative assessment

• Candidates should be reassured that committing to the MRCGP need not be a high risk strategy, financially or academically

• The tremendous commitment of the Panel of Examiners should be maintained

• The examination should be kept as economical as possible in any consideration of the resources of finance, time and effort required to service the examination

• The locus of control of the examination's destiny should be retained within the College

• The reputation of the examination and of the College for competence, integrity and excellence should be maintained.

More specifically it was felt essential that:

• The written papers should all be available on a single day

• The regulations should be made as clear and simple as possible

• The pricing structure should be very much fairer, with a fail in one section of the examination being no more expensive financially than a fail in any other

• The work involved in the video assessment of consulting skills could be reduced.

The seemingly radical response to these requirements is detailed in the rest of this book. The examination board believes that the new structure is simpler and more logical, and that it has dealt with some of the organisational inconsistencies that had previously crept in. The MRCGP examination is now easier to take but no easier to pass.

Evolution, not revolution

It is therefore clear that what appears to be radical change is, in fact, logical evolution. As previous candidates will have been all too aware, there has recently been a gradual blurring of some of the previous differences between the written papers. For instance, the CRQ began to use MCQ techniques, and the MEQ has used extended matching questions. This blurring has made it even more essential that the examination is 'blueprinted'. This technique has been recognized as being of increasing importance in medical assessment worldwide (Newble, 1994). Applied within the MRCGP initially by the former convenor of the panel, Professor Dame Lesley Southgate, and more recently by her successor, Dr Roger Neighbour, blueprinting defines the examination's content in the degree of detail necessary to infer appropriate test methods, and ensures that blindspots and duplication are avoided.

The new format

Since May 1998 the examination has consisted of four separate stand-alone modules. These are shown in Figure 2.1.

Figure 2.1   ***The modules in the MRCGP examination***

- Paper 1   (The written paper) A three-hour paper, combining elements of the pre-1998 modified essay question and the pre-1998 critical reading question papers

- Paper 2   (The MCQ) A three-hour machine-marked paper, combining elements of the pre-1998 multiple choice question of the critical reading question papers

- Consulting skills assessment:

                   Either: an assessment of seven video-taped consultations
                   Or: in exceptional circumstances, a simulated surgery

- Orals   Two 20-minute oral examinations

Pre-certification is required in cardio-pulmonary resuscitation and child health surveillance.

One major change which inevitably follows modularisation is that, for the first time since the early days of the MRCGP, every candidate is now examined in the orals, whereas in the past those with the lowest 15% of marks in the written papers were excluded. Candidates may now take the papers in any order, and as often as they like, but all modules must be taken within three years of the original starting date. Although many candidates, particularly GP registrars, continue to take all the modules in their final year of training, some choose to spread this out over a longer period.

The arrival of compulsory summative assessment, resulting in most GP registrars taking two separate assessments in their training year, has made many registrars and trainers feel that their training has been disrupted by assessment (Tegner, 1997). It is hoped that this anomaly will be ironed out, and discussions are continuing between the College and the JCPTGP about exemption from summative assessment for all successful candidates in the MRCGP, provided they have a satisfactory trainer's report.

One final result of modularisation was the disappearance of an identifiable cohort of candidates whose marks could be put in rank order so that the top 2.5% could be given distinction, as happened in the past. The examination board feels strongly that it is important to encourage candidates to do more than simply achieve a bare pass. Therefore the top 25-30% of candidates in each module are now awarded a pass with merit in that module. Candidates who pass all four modules with a merit in two are awarded a pass with merit. If they get merit in three or four modules, they are awarded MRCGP with distinction. This change is designed to encourage candidates to excel.

After all, assessment in a medical specialty should not simply be a means of assessing minimum competence, and the MRCGP is far more than that. It is becoming increasingly clear that patients and other health service professionals are expecting that general practitioners should have reached a high, rather than minimal, standard of competence. How can it be logical to accept low standards in the medical speciality which is the least supervised, the hardest to do well, and the easiest to do badly?

Future prospects

For those who hope that the examination will now stop changing, I would urge you to look at our history. As long as general practice develops this examination will develop too. In addition, the structural changes brought by modularisation also offer the potential for other benefits.

It is regrettable but true that many general practitioners are not members of the RCGP, and a survey of all general practitioners in the area of the Vale of Trent Faculty of the RCGP (Baker and Pringle 1995) showed that a substantial proportion of such doctors would be interested in joining it if there were an assessment process that was less threatening and more appropriate to their present situation than formal examination.

To meet this need Council promoted the introduction of membership by assessment of performance (MAP), which shares some features with the MRCGP exam and others with the College's fellowship by assessment system (FBA). The opportunities these assessment processes offer may appeal, for instance, to a doctor who wishes to become a member of the College and has a partner who intends to apply for Fellowship, for much of the preparatory work can be undertaken in parallel. Furthermore enthusiasts can now include their whole practices in the assessment through the quality practice award (QPA), for high quality practice depends on high quality support within the practice.

Indeed, it is possible that a modular structure will develop for post-MRCGP learning. For too long, passing the MRCGP has been seen as an end in itself. In the future, passing the MRCGP should be the start, not the end, of real membership of a real College. This theme is developed further in the final chapter, where the continuation of education after the MRCGP, and the opportunities presented by FBA and QPA are discussed.

Throughout these developments the examination board has been keen to make it transparently clear that no change in what candidates should study is expected. The MRCGP examination is designed to assess high quality practice. Those who devote their training to becoming high quality general practitioners will have used their time far better than those who cram or try simply to learn how to answer examination questions. The board has sought to preserve the reputation of the MRCGP examination for competence, integrity, and excellence. As the current president of the College, Denis Pereira Gray, then chairman of Council, wrote in 1990: 'The MRCGP examination is a living, dynamic institution, ready to review itself, ready to respond to the policies of the College as a whole, and ready to incorporate new ideas and new techniques in the light of evolving practice' (Lockie, 1990).

No one ever likes taking examinations, but it is hoped that this book should help the reader understand why this examination has developed in the way that it has, and how candidates and teachers can best prepare for it. For many years, the MRCGP examination has been seen as a corner stone of the College. As such, it is entirely appropriate that we should have attempted to combine the scientia of sound academic credentials with the caritas of candidate friendliness. As mottoes go, the College and the examination could not have asked for more.

References

Baker M, Pringle M (1995). Membership of the Royal College of General Practitioners by assessment: attitudes of members and non-members in one faculty area. *British Journal of General Practice* 45, 405-7.

Bingham L, Burrows P, Caird R, Holsgrove G, Jackson N (1996). Simulated surgery — using standardized patients to assess the clinical competence of GP Registrars. *Education for General Practice* 7, 102-111.

Hayden J (1996). Summative assessment — threat or opportunity? *British Journal of General Practice* 46, 132-133.

Joint Committee on Postgraduate Training for General Practice (1993) *Report*. London, JCPTGP.

Lockie C (1990). *Examination for Membership of the Royal College of General Practitioners (MRCGP) Occasional Paper 46*. London, RCGP.

Newble D, Dauphinee D, Dawson-Saunders B et al (1994) Guidelines for the development of effective and efficient procedures for the assessment of clinical competence. In Newble D, Jolly B, Wakeford R *The Certification and Recertification of Doctors.* Cambridge, Cambridge University Press.

Tegner H (1997) Summative assessment — a front line perspective. *Education for General Practice* 8, 95-100.

Wakeford R, Southgate L, Wass V (1995) Improving oral examinations: selecting, training, and monitoring examiners for the MRCGP. *British Medical Journal* 311, 931-5.

Walker J (1990). History of the MRCGP Examination. In: *Examination for Membership of the Royal College of General Practitioners (MRCGP). Occasional Paper 46.* London, RCGP.

3   The modular MRCGP examination in context

Roger Neighbour

The theoretical physicist Albert Einstein (so the story goes) kept permanently chalked on his blackboard at the Institute of Advanced Study at Princeton University this saying of George Pickering:

'Not everything that counts can be counted, and not everything that can be counted counts.'

General practitioners, who in their professional lives bring both scientific rigour and compassionate values to the service of their patients, will have an inkling of how for Einstein this paradox served as a useful check on his intellectual flights. The Royal College of General Practitioners captures something of the same sentiments in its motto *Cum scientia caritas*: 'With knowledge goes compassion'. It is no criticism of science to want it tempered with humanity, while caring can be a floppy virtue without the backbone of scientific discipline to keep it sturdy.

The MRCGP, perhaps more than any other postgraduate exam, seeks to balance both themes and to assess both kinds of ability in its candidates. My purpose in this chapter is to explain the exam's structures and procedures to intending candidates (see figure 3.1 page 24).

The thinking behind the modular structure may be more comprehensible, however, if first we reflect upon some of the contexts in which the exam exists. Five are worth distinguishing, though they overlap considerably:

- The quality of care delivered to patients
- The career of the individual candidate

- General practice as a profession
- The Royal College of General Practitioners
- The assessment of competence as an academic discipline.

Quality of patient care

The College and its examination are worth nothing unless they further the overarching purpose of raising the standard of general

---

Figure 3.1   The modular MRCGP

Four modules
Paper 1: — a 3-hour written paper in prose or short notes format
Paper 2: — a 3-hour machine-marked paper, largely in multiple choice
           format
Assessment of consulting skills:
           — 7 video-taped consultations
           — or (exceptionally) a simulated surgery
Orals   — two 20-minute orals

Two pre-certification requirements
Cardio-pulmonary resuscitation
Child health surveillance

Eligibility
Already eligible to undertake unsupervised general practice, or
Undergoing vocational training for general practice

Rules of credit accumulation
All four modules must be passed within three years of first applying
Modules can be taken all at once or separately, in any order
Up to three attempts at each module are allowed

Results
Each module may be failed, passed, or passed with merit
The exam overall may be failed, passed, passed with merit or passed
with distinction

---

practice being delivered in the nation's surgeries and consulting rooms. The MRCGP, being one of the main drivers of teaching and learning during vocational training, has a responsibility to ensure that the effort required to pass it has a worthwhile effect on patient care. In an ideal world we should like to know how close was the correlation between success in the MRCGP on the one hand and, on the other, quality markers of the care provided. Unfortunately, direct outcome measures are hard to come by in general practice.

The likely advent of revalidation, in which the College expects to play a significant role, should help to identify which are the most important professional competencies a GP should acquire and maintain. In the meantime, when it comes to the planning of its structure and detail, the exam makes every effort to ensure that the things it tests and the way it tests them are as valid as possible.

In the meantime, too, the MRCGP has gained respect in various important quarters as a hallmark of good practice. Several health authorities already require new principals in single-handed practice to possess the MRCGP, and the NHS Confederation is sympathetic to the College's own long-term aspiration that all new principals should be similarly qualified. Indeed, as the notion of a primary-care led national health service moves from concept to reality, we can expect more and more stakeholders — government, consumer organisations and professional bodies — to seek evidence that their trust in the specialty of clinical generalism is well placed.

General practice itself operates within several contexts simul-taneously, and the exam reflects them. Clinical medicine undergoes change. Norms of diagnosis and management evolve rapidly, and the abundance of information, both reliable and controversial, makes it hard to keep a perspective on what, at any given moment, constitutes best cost-effective practice. The more potent, invasive and expensive the intervention, the greater the need for professional decision-making to be up-to-date and critical.

Clinical idealism has to be tempered by social forces such as popular journalism, the rise of consumerism, litigiousness and calls for the greater accountability of the established professions. There are moral and ethical dimensions to virtually every problem presented to the GP. We are not immune to the knock-on and trickle-down effects of fiscal policy. Demand for NHS resources will always exceed the allocation, and, whatever the colour of the political landscape, no quart can be poured out of a pint pot.

Some critics of the MRCGP exam have suggested that a reasonable mark could be scored by anyone who, though not medically qualified, reads a daily broadsheet newspaper and a monthly journal of social comment. As long as cultural awareness is the framework for a thorough test of clinical competence, rather than a substitute for it, I do not consider this to be a shortcoming.

The MRCGP as a career milestone

The vast majority of candidates for the MRCGP are GP registrars who are undertaking, or who have recently completed, vocational training in the United Kingdom. College policy is for the exam to be expressly designed to assess the competencies young doctors at this stage of their careers might reasonably be expected to possess. The standard required to pass is higher than the minimal competence level tested by summative assessment whose function is primarily to protect patients from unacceptably poor or unsafe doctors. Success in the MRCGP is meant to indicate a superior level of attainment which the doctor can be proud of and which patients deserve and appreciate.

Although the regulations allow modules to be sat at any stage of training, the content of the examination is so rooted in everyday practice that many candidates will decide to sit it during the final months of their general practice attachment. The modular structure allows for the timing of the exam to be varied according to individual circumstances, however. Many registrars and trainers find the training year's agenda to be overcrowded, and protest that the abundance of assessment can be at the expense of fun, curiosity, reflection and 'time to stand and stare'.

Some candidates may, therefore, elect to take the multiple choice Paper 2 (which is predominantly a test of pure and applied knowledge) relatively early and to submit a video-tape for the consulting skills assessment during their registrar placement while they have easy access to patients, facilities and the help of a trainer, and to defer Paper 1 (the written paper) and the orals until they are established in a practice of their own.

Others may prefer to have a go at all four modules at once and get the exam 'under their belt' to mark their graduation from training and their readiness to assume the full responsibilities of a principal in general practice — a kind of rite of passage. In this case, taking the MRCGP has a more than surface similarity to the way medieval apprentices would submit examples of their work as a masterpiece in order, if the workmanship was good enough, to gain admittance to the ranks of their chosen craft guild.

An important sub-group of candidates practise overseas. Many take the MRCGP in order to enhance their own qualifications and to raise the profile and prestige of primary care in their own countries. Another significant minority of candidates are already established principals in Great Britain. Some undertake the exam as a self-imposed confirmation of their professional skill, while others may be expected to do so as part of preparation for becoming trainers. In the past some principals have found the exam unexpectedly difficult to pass, leading them understandably to question its credibility.

The origin of this apparent discrepancy lies in the different ways that new and experienced practitioners acquire and deploy their skill base. Mature doctors tend to have more of their knowledge 'below the water line', but by way of compensation often have a wider and more fluent repertoire of skills in consulting, organisation and high order decision-making.

To this latter group of potential candidates the modular format of the MRCGP should prove a welcome acknowledgement of their different learning and revision methods. The College now also offers membership by assessment of performance (MAP) as a non-exam based route to membership, which is described in chapters 10 and 11.

Whatever the individual decision or motivation, the MRCGP examination is positioned as a quality marker held in high and wide esteem, reflecting well upon the credentials of the successful candidate. Its eclectic range of component modules, testing across the whole range of knowledge, skills, values and competencies needed in modern general practice, combined with the flexibility provided by the modular format, can have a motivating effect on a young GP's career which is far more helpful than it is intrusive — in other words, more a milestone than a millstone.

The profession of general practice

To their admirers, professions are self-regulating and high-principled institutions dedicated to the service of people in need. The deal is that, in exchange for public esteem and high earnings, a profession undertakes to set self-referenced criteria for the entry of new recruits and to guarantee the performance of its established members.

Historically, such voluntary self-accountability has afforded naïve or unprincipled doctors the chance to cut corners or compromise standards. George Bernard Shaw, you may recall, described professions as 'conspiracies against the laity', while the philosopher Ivan Illich considered them to be malevolent cartels of vested interest, arrogantly exploiting people's frailty and undermining their natural resilience for their own aggrandisement.

There is a grain of truth in even this most cynical of viewpoints, and it is to the credit of the medical profession that in recent years we have been proactive in establishing procedures which safeguard both patients and doctors themselves from inadequate levels of competence. The General Medical Council (whose president at the time of writing is Sir Donald Irvine, a former GP and chairman of the RCGP Council) is the fulcrum of medical self-regulation. Its performance procedures now provide for the identification of doctors whose clinical standards have fallen unacceptably. As far as general practice is concerned, the 1976 NHS Vocational Training Act and the various regulations that stemmed from it established the present framework whereby qualifying standards for GP registrars are now set by the Joint Committee on Postgraduate Training for General Practice (JCPTGP) through the mechanism of summative assessment. The JCPTGP is a joint venture between the RCGP and the General Practitioners Committee of the British Medical Association, and as such represents an alliance between the academic strength of the College and the organisational and medico-political strengths of the BMA to patrol the entry points to general practice. (The MRCGP's relationship to summative assessment remains unresolved as I write, a sad testimony to our profession's capacity for internecine rivalry.) Revalidation, though still in the discussion stage, will ensure that the commitment to continuing professional education which starts with the MRCGP continues, we hope seamlessly, where the examination leaves off.

The Royal College of General Practitioners

Examiners, as we constantly try to reassure candidates, are human beings, and we feel proud when we sometimes hear the examination described as 'the jewel in the College's crown'. If this phrase is meant to signify a belief that, *magnum in parva*, the exam encapsulates the values of the wider College, aspiring to foster excellence in all the domains of general practice in the interests of patient care, then perhaps some of that pride might be forgiven.

The RCGP Council takes ultimate accountability for all aspects of the examination — from the detailed consideration of questions and marking schedules through to issues of strategy and policy. In practice, most issues are dealt with by the examination board, part of the College's assessment network. The examination board (see figure 3.2 page 30) is chaired by an elected member of Council, who usually also has experience as an examiner. All strands of the exam are represented, though with the present exception of candidates! In addition, non-examiner members of Council represent the good offices of the College. The exam draws on the expertise of outside consultants who advise on psychometric and statistical matters and who have links with the wider disciplines of test methodology and the assessment of medical competence. Administratively the exam is serviced by permanent members of the College staff.

Figure 3.2.   **The Examination Board of Council**

Chairman
(Elected member of Council)

Members
3 appointed members of Council
Convenor of the Panel of Examiners
3 elected representatives of the panel

Observers
Module convenors:
Paper 1
Paper 2
Clinical component (video and simulated surgery)
Orals

By invitation
Consultants to the panel
Representative of Association of Course Organisers
Representative of directors of postgraduate GP education
Representative of membership by assessment of performance
Representative of the patient liaison group

In attendance
Head and deputy head of the examination department

Whatever credibility the examination possesses is in large measure due to the quality and vitality of the Panel of Examiners. At present, there are about 150 examiners from all over the United Kingdom, practising in a wide range of settings. All, even those working in academic departments of general practice, are in active practice for at least three sessions a week. Many have experience of vocational training and continuing medical education through their work as trainers, course organisers or GP tutors. The selection, training and quality control of examiners is discussed later in this chapter.

Candidates should be reassured that the content and processes of the MRCGP are devised and implemented not from any ivory tower but by the collaboration of a large cohort of 'jobbing' GPs fully alive to the challenges and constraints of real-life practice.

The academic context of the examination

There is an enormous body of world literature and experience relating to the assessment of clinical competence. The MRCGP draws heavily on it to ensure the respectability of its procedures and also regularly makes significant contributions to the expertise both at home and abroad. Candidates who invest time, effort and money in taking a postgraduate examination, and whose careers may be affected by the result, are entitled to satisfactory answers to a number of pertinent questions.

Is the exam valid?

In other words, does it test the sorts of things that are relevant to practice in the real world? Are the methods used to test them likely to deliver a reasonable assessment? Does passing the exam mean someone is a good GP? There is no strict syllabus or core curriculum for general practice, and few agreed outcome measures. The MRCGP validates its content largely through the credibility of its examiners as GPs in active practice.

The examination blueprint described below should be considered as the measure of its relevance. The exam's choice of test formats is under constant review in the light both of advances in best international practice and feedback from candidates and other interested parties.

Is it reliable?

Can the individual candidate trust the accuracy of his or her results? Suppose that the questions had been different? Would it have made any significant difference if the examination had been sat on a different occasion, or marked by different examiners? Or, if it had been marked by the same examiners but on a different occasion? And what happens to those borderline candidates whose performance comes within a whisker of the pass mark? Any test can examine only a fraction of the potential subject matter and the candidate's knowledge of it.

An examination is analogous to taking multiple biopsies from the whole range of the candidate's abilities, and making a diagnosis on the strength of the histological report. The reliability of the resulting decisions is the subject of constant and intense statistical scrutiny, drawing on the branch of statistics known as generalisability theory.

Appropriate indices of correlation, reliability and internal consistency are regularly monitored and compare extremely favourably with other equivalent exams throughout the world. For instance, in written papers, a value of Cronbach's coefficient α (an indicator of reliability) of >0.8 is generally regarded as acceptable. The MRCGP regularly performs well in excess of this level.

Is the exam fair?

In the past, the MRCGP was a largely peer-referenced examination. In its purest form this means that the individual candidate is compared with all the others sitting the exam and a decision made as to what proportion of candidates should pass. In the pre-modular MRCGP the pass rate was about 73%. This policy can be made consistent if (as was the case) steps are taken to establish whether or not the overall standard of a given cohort of candidates has varied, but it offends a sense of natural justice which prefers a passing standard to be established which every candidate could potentially attain. In the present exam the standard required of the individual to pass each module is devised so as to be independent of the performance of other candidates as far as is possible.

Every examination has to decide its policy towards candidates whose performance falls close to the pass mark (say, to within a standard error of measurement of it). To err on the side of generosity means passing some individuals who, had they been tested on another occasion, might have failed. If on the other hand a policy of 'no bad apples at any price' operates, some will fail who might otherwise have passed.

The College wishes be as inclusive as possible, and its policy to borderline candidates reflects this, with the proviso that even borderline candidates passing as a result of this generosity will have been judged above the level of minimum competence representing safety to practise. A sub-standard performance in one element of the exam can not be compensated by doing extra well in another. All modules must be passed in their own right. Most people consider this to be fair; in general practice clumsy interpersonal skills should not be overlooked merely because the doctor happens to be the world's expert on pityriasis rosea. Full details of the standard-setting processes are not given here as they may change from time to time, but are published in the current examination regulations sent to all candidates.

The structure and processes of any institution stem from its history and should be the servants of its function. I hope that, against the background I have described in this chapter, the details of the examination will make more sense and will help potential candidates the better to orientate their preparation.

Please note that although these details are correct at the time of going to press, the examination board reserves the right to make alterations to the format and content of the examination. Up-to-date regulations are published well before each session of the exam, sent to all candidates at the time they apply, and are available on request from the examination department. You should ensure that you have a copy of the regulations current for the time you sit any of the exam's modules, particularly if some time has elapsed since you first applied.

The modular MRCGP

Eligibility

Any doctor who is eligible to be an independent practitioner of general practice or family medicine, or who is undergoing vocational training with this in view, is eligible to sit the MRCGP. Candidates already eligible for independent practice must supply evidence of this at the time of applying for the exam. In the United Kingdom this may be either the Certificate of Prescribed or Equivalent Experience, issued by the JCPTGP, or confirmation of the candidate's number on the principals list of a health authority or board. Candidates eligible to practise outside the UK must provide a copy of their licence or equivalent document, with an attested translation if necessary.

Candidates who are still undergoing vocational training may apply for and sit the examination. If successful, however, they will not be eligible to take up College membership until they have received a Certificate of Prescribed or Equivalent Experience.

Although the exam may be taken at any stage of vocational training, it should be borne in mind that all modules are designed to be appropriate to the experience of doctors in active general practice.

The examination rules

There are four modules:

Paper 1:	A three-hour written paper in prose or short notes format
Paper 2:	A three-hour machine-marked paper, largely in multiple-choice format

An assessment of consulting skills based on:

Seven video-taped consultations **or**

A simulated surgery, in exceptional circumstances

An oral examination:

comprising two 20-minute orals.

- You must pass all four modules in order to pass the examination overall
- The modules may be taken at the same session or at different sessions, in any order. You do not need to have passed the written papers before taking the oral
- You may have up to two further attempts at each module (on payment of a supplementary re-sit fee)
- All modules must be passed within three years of acceptance of your application, otherwise you must retake the whole examination
- You must also supply evidence, in a form prescribed by the examination, of proficiency in basic cardio-pulmonary resuscitation and child health surveillance.

Each module is more fully described in later chapters of this book. A brief summary of each now follows.

The written papers

Papers 1 and 2 are available twice a year, in May and October. They are timetabled on the same day (Paper 1, the written paper, in the morning and Paper 2, the multiple choice paper, in the afternoon) for the convenience of candidates who want to take both at the same session, but they can be taken or retaken singly.

The written papers are offered in up to 10 centres nationwide and by arrangement in Germany, Hong Kong and Saudi Arabia. Papers 1 and 2 between them assess pure and applied knowledge, decision-making, critical appraisal and the evidence base of general practice.

The consulting skills component

The usual method of testing consulting skills calls for the submission of a videotape of seven consultations with patients, who have given their consent, together with an annotated workbook providing a commentary on the recorded consultations. Up to seven examiners will assess whether the candidate satisfactorily meets a range of pre-notified performance criteria.

There are summer and winter marking sessions for the video recordings each year. Detailed instructions for preparing and submitting video tapes, together with the workbook and sample patient consent form, are obtainable from the examination department.

Video recording is the normal method of assessing consulting skills for the MRCGP. An alternative, the simulated surgery, is provided for candidates who, in the opinion of the convenor of the Panel of Examiners, have insuperable difficulties in making video recordings. These might include documented moral or religious objection, or where the doctor usually consults in a language other than English, or where personal circumstances make it impossible to have access to suitable patients. If you consider you may be eligible to sit the simulated surgery rather than the video assessment, please refer to the regulations for guidance on how to proceed.

The simulated surgery consists of a series of consultations with actors who role play patients. It, too, is available twice a year, usually during the period of the oral examinations. Because of the logistics involved in running a simulated surgery, the number of candidates accepted for this form of consulting skills assessment may have to be limited. A candidate accepted for simulated surgery who had the module deferred for this reason would be granted an extension to the time allowed to accumulate passes in all the exam's modules.

Certificates of competence in CPR and CHS must be submitted at the time of applying for the consulting skills module.

The oral examination

The oral examination, in fact, consists of two separate orals each lasting 20 minutes and conducted by a pair of examiners. There is a break of five minutes between them while the first examiners award their grades. After the second oral, all four examiners meet to review the candidate's performance and to agree an overall result for the oral module.

The aim of the orals is to assess the candidate's decision-making, and the professional values underpinning it, in the contexts of:

- The care of patients
- Working with colleagues
- The social role of general practice
- The doctor's personal responsibilities.

Professional values include such things as respect for the evidence base of practice, effectiveness and cost-effectiveness, respect for patients' autonomy, caritas, self-awareness, the ethical framework of practice, and commitment to high and sustained standards of practice. The examiners will be looking for evidence that the candidate's approaches are coherent, rational, ethical and sensitive.

The examination blueprint

Theoretically, the starting point for any assessment should be a comprehensive description of the curriculum, ie a full account of the knowledge, skills and attributes considered necessary for competent performance of the task in question. General practice not only lacks any such agreed core curriculum, it almost makes a virtue of the vastness of its territory and the fluidity of its boundaries.

Nonetheless, the MRCGP uses a working blueprint, developed from the collective opinions of the Panel of Examiners, when devising components in order to ensure that the exam as far as possible reflects the range and diversity of practice in Britain today. Blueprinting also provides a safeguard against inadvertent blind spots and reduplications in the mix of questions.

The current version of the MRCGP blueprint is shown in figure 3.3 on page 38. It consists of a list of domains described in general terms, which the exam convenors use to plan the detail of the various components.

Figure 3.4 on page 39 shows how the domains are allocated or mapped from the blueprint to the individual modules. The allocations shown represent differences in emphasis, and should not be taken as inflexible. Within each module, a variety of contexts will be examined in order to test an appropriate range and depth.

It might be helpful to candidates preparing for the exam to expand this blueprint by considering also the various roles the general practitioner fulfils. (See figure 3.5, page 40) A two-dimensional grid then could be imagined, with the blueprint domains down one axis and the list of roles along the other, giving a more detailed map of the territory assessed in the examination.

The examiners, it should be noted, are not overly enamoured of such artificial devices. Nevertheless, the exercise may give a flavour of the breadth of subjects lying within the compass of the MRCGP.

Examination results

Results in each module are reported in writing to candidates as a fail, pass or pass with merit. A pass list is also posted on the

Figure 3.3   The MRCGP modular blueprint

Domains — generalisable skills, attributes & competencies

A   Factual knowledge

B   Evolving knowledge: uncertainty, 'hot' topics, qualitative research

C   The evidence base of practice: knowledge of literature, quantitative research

D   Critical appraisal skills: interpretation of literature, principles of statistics

E   Application of knowledge: justification, prioritising, audit

F   Problem solving: general applications

G   Problem solving: case-specific clinical management

H   Personal care: matching principles to individual patients

I   Written communication

J   Verbal communication: the consultation process

K   The practice context: team issues, practice management, business skills

L   The regulatory framework of practice

M   The wider context: medico-political, legal and societal issues

N   Ethnic and trans-cultural issues

O   Values and attitudes: ethics, integrity, consistency, caritas

P   Self-awareness: insight, reflective learning, 'the doctor as person'

Q   Commitment to maintaining standards: personal and professional growth, continuing medical education

College's Internet website: http://www.rcgp.org.uk. Under the rules of credit accumulation up to three attempts are allowed at each module. If one or more modules has not been passed after three attempts the whole examination will have been failed. Further attempts can also be made at any module(s) which have been passed in order to gain a pass with merit. In this case it is the best and not the last result which counts.

Figure 3.4. **Blueprints of individual modules**

Domains

Paper 1	A, B, C, D, E, F, G, H, I, (J), K, M, N, (P)
Paper 2	A, B, C, (D), G, L, N
Consulting skills	G, H, J, (O)
Orals	D, E, F, (G), H, J, K, M, (N), O, P, Q
NB	Domains indicated by letters in brackets are relevant to those modules, but are principally examined in others

---

To pass the MRCGP examination overall requires at least a pass in all four modules within three years of the initial application to sit the exam.

Results in all modules will be issued at the same time, after the summer and winter sessions of the exam. In order to ensure accuracy and confidentiality and prevent excessive demands on the examination department staff, results will not be communicated or discussed by telephone. Any enquiries must be made in writing.

Directors of postgraduate education have an understandable wish to learn how candidates from their region have fared in the exam, as

---

Figure 3.5   *Roles of the general practitioner*

Clinician	Family physician	Authority figure
Confidant	Patient's advocate	Gatekeeper
Resource allocator	Handler of information	Team member
Team leader	Partner	Colleague
Employer	Manager	Business-person
Learner	Teacher	Reflective practitioner
Researcher	Agent and shaper of social policy	Moral agent
Member of a profession	Private individual	Human being

---

part of their own internal audit of vocational training. Some also like to welcome the successful as new members of the College. While the College has no wish to breach candidates' confidentiality, permission will be sought at the time of application to release pass lists in a form suitable for these purposes.

Merit and distinction

Before the MRCGP went modular, about the top 2.5% of candidates were awarded a pass with distinction. The main motivating force for most candidates in the all-or-nothing exam was the fear of failure. However, there is a danger in a modular exam that candidates might aspire no higher than to settle for a bare pass in all modules, which runs counter to the exam's ambitions to encourage high standards across the board. The modular MRCGP therefore distinguishes an overall pass, a pass with merit and a pass with distinction. A pass with merit will be awarded to approximately the top 20% to 25% of candidates taking each module. Candidates achieving merit in two modules (and who pass the other two) will be awarded an overall pass with merit. Candidates achieving merit in all four modules, or in three with a pass in the fourth, will be awarded an overall pass with distinction.

The Fraser Rose Medal is awarded annually to the candidate who, in the opinion of the examiners, has given the best performance in the examination in the preceding year. It is usually presented at the College's annual general meeting.

Feedback, complaints, appeals and special circumstances

The MRCGP is, in educational terms, a summative assessment and not a formative one. That is to say, its purpose is to make a judgement rather than to provide educational feedback to individual candidates on their performance. When notified of their results, candidates receive a statement of their own marks or grades, the pass and merit marks, the pass rate for each module and, in the case of the video component, of any performance criteria that have been failed. A number of candidates after each session of the exam ask for additional explanations of why they may have failed. Often their letters express sheer incredulity; others consider there were extenuating circumstances which impaired their performance; some suspect arithmetical or computer errors in processing their marks and a few complain of biased or unsympathetic examining.

The convenor deals personally with all such correspondence. However, with up to 2000 candidates taking the exam each year, it is simply not feasible to provide a detailed individual commentary on performance in the written papers or consulting skills component. A summary of oral examiners' comments may be disclosed at the convenor's discretion.

Any candidate who wishes to lodge an appeal or complaint, or to bring to the examiners' attention any factors or events that may have had an adverse effect on his or her performance, must do so in writing to the convenor within 14 days of receiving notification of the results. The examination takes seriously its reputation for fairness and candidate friendliness, and the convenor will attempt to resolve dissatisfaction wherever possible. However, the exam's modules are marked, and passing standards set, in accordance with current best international practice, and procedures are so constituted as to reduce the impact of isolated vagaries in marking to a level considered negligible by the College. Unless there is good reason to suspect a procedural error, the exam makes no provision to re-mark written papers, reassess performance in the consulting skills component or reassign grades in the orals.

The College operates a formal appeals procedure, details of which are given in the regulations supplied to and agreed by all candidates. The remedies for legitimate grievances are largely confined to explanation, refunding or waiving examination fees, or extension of the time limits for completing the exam.

The examination is willing, where possible, to adapt its procedures to the needs of candidates suffering from permanent or temporary disability such as illness, injury, pregnancy or dyslexia. Candidates affected by any such issues should bring them, in writing, to the attention of the convenor at the earliest possible opportunity.

Quality control in the examination

The text of this chapter has combined idealism and technical small print, and in this it parallels the skill-mix of the MRCGP examination itself. To return for a moment to its opening quotation: the exam aspires to measure what matters in primary care — to count reliably what is countable, and to take full account of what is hard to count. Because there is necessarily a significant element of human discretion and judgement in assessing the sophisticated skills required for general practice, the examination builds into its organisation a range of quality control measures which compares favourably with any examination in the world.

For their part, candidates are entitled to cap the College's Latin motto with a tag of their own: *Quis custodiet ipsos custodes?* — Who is to police the police themselves? The Panel of Examiners — their commitment, credibility and professional experience — is at once the exam's greatest asset and potentially its weakest link. This final section therefore explains how the panel, through the selection, training and monitoring of its members, tries to remain worthy of the respect in which the MRCGP is held.

Examiner selection

Potential new examiners (PNEs) must have been principals in general practice for at least five years, and must work a minimum of three sessions a week in NHS practice. They must have passed the MRCGP exam within the past 10 years or, if not, must resit it. The qualities required of a PNE include:

- Adequate and up-to-date knowledge and clinical and professional skills
- Professional credibility and esteem
- Courteousness and sensitivity
- Reliability (in both statistical and behavioural senses)
- The ability to make consistent and unbiased judgements
- The ability to discriminate and rank-order candidates' responses
- Inter-personal and small group effectiveness
- The ability to think on one's feet.

PNEs are allowed to nominate themselves, but three confidential references are required from:

- A current examiner
- An officer of their College faculty board
- A director of postgraduate GP education or GP tutor
- A Fellow of the RCGP
- A partner in their own practice.

PNEs attend the oral examinations for two days to observe and learn. During this time they answer a recent Paper 2, the multiple choice test of factual knowledge, in order to establish the adequacy of their knowledge base, and must achieve a passing score. They then attend an assessment day conducted by experienced members of the panel, where they are assessed for the ability to devise and apply marking schedules, work in groups, assess video tapes and conduct orals. If successful at this stage they then become full members of the panel. New examiners undergo further training in oral examining and participate in the annual examiners' workshop.

On-going quality control

Validity and reliability in the written modules are fostered by the piloting of written questions and papers among the whole panel, by using index scripts and tele-conferencing to calibrate the markers of individual questions, and by comprehensive statistical analysis of marking data.

There are regular training sessions for oral and video examiners. Each day's oral examining begins with a group viewing of an excerpt from a recent oral examination in order to encourage uniformity of judgement. Examiners have a session of their oral examining video-recorded and critiqued at the start of their examining careers and again at roughly two-year intervals thereafter. A proportion of the oral examiners present on any given day observe their colleagues' performance and give feedback. Candidates' comments sent to the convenor, where they relate to individual examiners, are passed to the examiner concerned.

Finally, the MRCGP regularly sends representatives to national and international meetings of experts such as the European Academy of Teachers of General Practice (EURACT) and the Cambridge Conferences on Medical Assessment. There are frequent exchanges of ideas with other British royal colleges and with primary care examinations in Europe, North America, Australia and New Zealand, and the exam often hosts visitors from other colleges and academic institutions.

4   Approaching College membership

Richard Moore

As one of the medical royal colleges, the Royal College of General Practitioners is a professional association of doctors in primary care whose purpose is to foster and maintain the highest possible standards. In its examination for membership the underlying question the examiners are asking is: has this candidate demonstrated that standard of competence in general practice which justifies full membership of the College?

In ensuring the answer to that question is an unequivocal 'yes', candidates must know what will be required of them to reach that high standard as independent, unsupervised practitioners in a complex and demanding profession. This begs the question: what is general practice? Although there are many styles and versions of general practice which vary with place, population, priorities and personnel, it is possible to identify some of its characteristics in contrast to other medical disciplines. These characteristics determine the attributes which a general practitioner must possess to achieve competence, and as such will feature prominently in the examination. Approaching the MRCGP as an exercise in preparation for independent practice will enable you to take it in your stride.

Candidates for membership by assessment of performance (MAP) will already be well down the road outlined in this chapter, for much of MAP is the demonstration that the attributes expected of a member of the College have already been acquired. Nevertheless, because much of what follows concerns the idea that improvement in competence is a consequence of a systematic reflection upon experience, it may encourage learning in that way. Ideas that flow from the rationale and structure of the exam, such as the blueprint and the domains described in chapter 3, are not specific to the exam but derived from general practice itself, and may help MAP candidates to develop their own agendas for development as they prepare to be assessed.

The wide scope of general practice

Clearly, much of the content of the exam is concerned with clinical competence in the familiar areas of diagnosis, investigation and treatment, including an understanding of procedures which may be carried out in other places such as hospitals or social services departments. Such matters feature prominently in the blueprint. It goes without saying that it is essential to have a sound knowledge base of clinical science, also of practice management and medico-legal matters, but there is much more to competence in general practice than mere possession of such knowledge.

The challenge that faces the new principal in general practice is how to identify and manage significant issues in an environment that is personal, domestic or social rather than the clinically oriented circumstances of hospital, where the training common to all disciplines mostly takes place. The knowledge needed to diagnose and treat a straightforward clinical condition may be much the same wherever it occurs, but the subtleties of management may vary greatly in different circumstances, while the modes of presentation and the options for intervention can differ widely. Furthermore, factors that are not purely clinical, such as the needs of relatives, or home or employment circumstances, and poverty or prosperity have a great bearing on how cases are managed in primary care. Nor is that care confined to clinical situations alone. Presentations in primary care are often ill defined; hidden agendas are common, and apparently trivial matters may conceal important problems. Finding the significance is not a simple task

The RCGP has a job description of the general practitioner (RCGP 1972) which begins: 'The general practitioner is a doctor who provides personal, primary and continuing care to individuals and families...' Note the emphasis on the words personal and continuing. Other important features of this description are given in figure 4.1 (page 47).

Figure 4.1   *Some features of the RCGP job description of a general practitioner*

- Care is personal, primary and continuing
- There is co-operation with a range of specialists
- The GP is part of a team, even though single handed
- Diagnosis is made in physical, psychological and social terms. It is given in patients' homes, the consulting room and sometimes in hospital
- Responsibility is taken for making initial decisions in every problem that is presented
- Intervention may be therapeutic, educational or preventive

Responsibilities in several important areas not found in other disciplines play a significant part in the day-to-day work of general practitioners and their colleagues. It is therefore necessary to identify these characteristics at an early stage in preparation for general practice, so that opportunities can be sought to gain experience in them and orientate thinking in their direction. For instance:

• The care given may be in patients' own homes, not just the community but where people, the patient and others, actually live, sleep, eat work and play

• The GP must make an initial decision in every problem, which may be an emergency or other critical situation, or something apparently trivial. Even if it is decided to do nothing this must be a positive decision. This necessitates understanding the true problem which is not necessarily the one that was presented

• The doctor works in a team, which includes co-operation with specialists and others in different places of work, as well as having a relationship with patients individually

• Education of patients and others is an essential part of the work

• Preservation of health and prevention of disease are important duties, as well as the treatment of existing illness

• Social factors, such as lifestyle, employment and poverty are relevant to the management of individual cases and the practice as a whole.

In addition, the general practitioner's work includes other important characteristics which must be developed in preparation for independent practice. Along with the job description, these characteristics were published in the College's seminal document on the educational needs of general practice, *The Future General Practitioner* (RCGP 1972), and though written nearly 30 years ago still remain valid because they are central to the concept of primary care. Eleven goals of the general practitioner were identified, some of which are contained in the job description already referred to. Others are shown in figure 4.2. Some of them are obvious, such as the breadth of diagnosis and the importance of social factors in health, and though there is little debate about the uniqueness of the individual on the one hand, and the generalness of the practitioner on the other, their importance should not be underestimated.

Figure 4.2   *Some educational goals for the general practitioner*

- Recognize that patients are unique individuals
- Know how to use time appropriately
- Understand how interpersonal relationships in families can affect health and illness
- Understand the impact of social factors on health and disease
- Command a range of options for intervention
- Manage a practice properly
- Identify continuing educational needs
- Be able to audit his or her own work effectively
- Be aware of the implications for the practice of relevant research

---

Time is a resource which can be precious. Used skilfully and carefully time can be productive, yet if wasted can be costly in terms of opportunity and money. It is important to develop a sense of when to take plenty of time to pursue a problem, when to be patient and wait for events, or how to allow adequate time for an important task when feeling under pressure to attend to other matters.

Recent work has shown how the outcome of consultations is affected by the time taken with patients, especially where problems are complex, or where they are complicated by language differences, or where problems have a large psychological content (Howie 1999). Equally important is the need to have a range of options for managing a situation and the ability to choose between them appropriately. What suits one case may be unacceptable or totally wrong in another, so the doctor must be able to find the best procedure from a variety of choices.

A big change which will meet a new principal in general practice is the need to manage the practice efficiently and effectively. Unlike most hospital doctors, the general practitioner has a business to run, and the income it provides depends on the quality of its management. The team that works within the business, the resources available to it and the way they are used are all part of this and, as the proprietors of the business, the partners of the practice have responsibility for its organisation. This cannot be delegated to others. The policy of the practice and how to implement it, staff requirements, conformity with the law in general and relating to medicine in particular, as with drug stocks, health and safety and employment law, all have to be understood by the principals.

With the increase in responsibility and accountability for developing practices through primary care groups there is now a greater need to be original and innovative, and at the same time effective and accountable. Many doctors now look towards salaried, part-time and long-term locum employment in general practice, but even for these an understanding of practice policies and management systems is important to ensure an efficient and effective service. Such an understanding cannot be achieved without thinking about the kind of broad issues that reach beyond the purely clinical field into the context of the society in which people live, work and play, and sometimes need the help of the medical services.

General practice in a social context

Beyond the practice is the population it serves, which is, of course, much wider than just the list of patients. The town, the city or the countryside where the practice is situated has its own health needs, and a variety of pressures and demands in respect of which general practitioners have a duty to the population as a whole as well as their specific patients who are part of it.

Whether or not they become involved as political or social activists GPs must understand the social and cultural ideas and circumstances of all their patients even if they do not share them. Differences in social class, culture, religion, educational attainment, and racial origins are important factors. If change towards a healthier lifestyle is needed, it is necessary to know the existing state and the social and personal factors that will help or hinder the proposed changes.

As an illustration of the diversity of fields that GPs may be involved in, consider some of the following:

- Health education: does it reach the people who need it most? If not, why not?
- Regional and social class differences in smoking-related diseases
- Immigrant populations and ethnic minorities
- Eating-related disorders
- Child abuse
- Alcohol and drug dependence

No effective action can be taken about these problems without the views of society being taken into account, not least because society funds most of the medical services. Medicine is now a major consumer of the nation's resources, which must be used wisely both at the level of the population as a whole and of the individual doctor-patient interaction. In deciding the priorities within the practice, whether clinical, preventive or educational, the general practitioner must know and understand the characteristics of the population that the practice serves.

Society also determines the rules within which we all operate, which are reflected in legal constraints and ethical conventions. The legal constraints are both those imposed specifically on doctors, such as the laws governing the use of medicines and the care of the mentally ill, and those which apply generally. Some ethical considerations, like issues of confidentiality, consent and euthanasia, concern the population as a whole, while others relate to the profession in particular such as the relationship with medical colleagues or other professionals.

At the end of training, a registrar may well feel that much has been accomplished, and that the time has come for a slower pace of learning. Medical progress will not wait, however, and soon the new principal will have to address the question of continuing education. How are learning needs to be identified? How can they be met? What has been good and what not so good about the practice in general and his or her work in particular? What new research has been published and what implications does it carry? Is change needed, and if so how is it to be managed and by whom? Without such change doctors and practices risk becoming ineffective, even unsafe, so the identification of learning needs is an important priority.

Self-awareness: the key to preparation

The time available to prepare for the exam is short. Much ground must be covered at the same time as gaining experience by contributing to the clinical work of a practice. The exam is not an end in itself, however, but one step on the longer road of professional self-development, a theme that has been touched on by David Haslam in chapter 2 and is taken further in chapter 12. A well-prepared candidate is, therefore, one who has a good knowledge of clinical science and the ability to apply it, and has begun the habit of reflecting upon and learning from experience. It is through experience that adults learn.

This does not mean just ploughing on attempting to solve the problems as they occur, but taking time to study and reflect upon selected events and the way they were managed. Experience in itself is a poor teacher, except perhaps to reveal that some things are fun and others painful. To be instructive experience must be reflected upon to discover what actually happened, how and why it occurred, so that future activity can be modified accordingly.

Such learning may be formalised in the process of audit, that is: 'the attempt to improve the quality of medical care by measuring the performance of those providing that care, considering the performance in relation to desired standards, and by improving on those standards' (Marinker 1990). Inherent in this statement is the concept of standard. How good is good? Only by comparing what is ideal with what is practicable and striving to make the two the same can we reach the highest standard.

Not every activity can be subjected to formal audit however, nor is it always practicable within the constraints of the registrar year, but every activity can be analysed to discover what attributes the doctor needs to meet its demands. This may be done by the doctor alone, or with others in situations such as tutorials, small group discussion with peers, and critical event analysis with colleagues, including those in other disciplines. In the context of preparing for the exam such reflection should relate the event in question to the blueprint of the exam, thereby enabling confidence to grow in areas where the doctor is already competent and blindspots to be identified and remedied.

Let us consider some examples. Figure 4.3 (see page 53)shows some common situations where several domains in the blueprint are relevant. In contemplating such cases, it would be a useful exercise to review one's competence in each domain and, if necessary, take steps to improve it. In situation 1, a patient has been to four different doctors for the same condition. There may be good reasons for this, such as a series of emergencies or night calls, or the absence of a doctor on leave. If it happens once or twice it may not matter, but if more often there may be problems. What, then, is your attitude to continuity of care? Is it important to the patient? To you? What problems may arise from discontinuity? How could problems that arise be resolved? Read and talk about how others deal with the matter, and think about your own attitude and how it can be implemented.

However good your consulting skills (assessment of which forms one whole module in the exam), a consultation will sometimes go wrong, as in situation 2. You should ask why. Was there a misunderstanding? If so, how did that happen? Was it your choice of language, too technical, too many long words, or too rushed because you assumed that the patient would understand. Or, was it the patient's understanding which was at fault; did she have poor language skills, or different cultural ideas? Examine your own performance to learn about your consulting skills.

Figure 4.3   ***Some situations and relevant domains***

Situation	*Relevant domains*
1 A patient has seen four doctors for the same condition	O Values and attitudes, consistency, caritas K Practice context, team issues
2 An unsatisfactory consultation	J Verbal communication N Ethnic & transcultural issues
3 Terminal care	G Problem-solving, clinical management H Personal care, ethics eg euthanasia
4 Audit: choosing topics and standards	A Factual knowledge C Evidence base, knowledge of literature & research E Application of knowledge, audit Q Commitment to maintaining standards, personal & professional growth, CME

A case like situation 3 may contain clinical challenges you have not met before. A patient is dying in distress. What is the cause of the distress? How can it be alleviated? How much are you prepared to be involved personally? If the patient asks you 'not to let me suffer', how do you know whether this means he is covertly asking for euthanasia, and if it does how will you respond? What do you know of the legal situation, and practice elsewhere in the world?

Situation 4 brings you back to the area of factual knowledge, but in a new and possibly uncertain field. You choose to audit some area of your work (not just for the purpose of assessment but because it is an excellent form of self-directed learning). To do this thoroughly you must meet several requirements such as:

- Know the accepted facts about the condition
- Get up-to-date information from recent research
- Know how to carry out an audit properly
- Have adequate records about your activities in the topic in question
- Describe the standard of care you expect to achieve in it
- Commit yourself to change where necessary

If all these are met successfully you are likely to grow in professional competence as well as receiving a boost to your self-esteem.

A variety of roles

In chapter 3 Roger Neighbour touched on the wide variety of roles of the general practitioner. His suggests no less than 24 different roles that GPs may be called upon to play at different times, and with some thought others could be added even to this comprehensive list. It is therefore important, in approaching the exam, and the independent practice that will follow it, to identify these roles as they occur. They will not all occur simultaneously, but several may be needed to deal with a particular situation. Two of these are considered in figure 4.4 (see page 55).

In situation 1 a patient comes late in the day with a difficult problem just as you hope to go home, which is all too familiar to anyone with the slightest experience of general practice. It puts the doctor in a difficulty by creating a conflict between the personal and professional roles, as well as requiring the fulfilment of others. The problem needs an initial decision (clinician role); can the doctor empathise with the patient as another human being? Could, or should, someone else deal with this problem more appropriately (team member)? Does the patient need referral (gatekeeper)? And so on.

As a registrar you may not be asked to chair a meeting about a practice initiative such as a stop-smoking policy, as in situation 2, though perhaps it would be a good exercise and there is nothing to stop you imagining yourself doing so. What role does the chairman fulfil? He or she will have to be several things at the same time — authority figure and team member, resource allocator and business person — and these may be in conflict with each other. How can these duties be met, and the conflicts within them resolved?

Figure 4.4   *Situations requiring various roles of the general practitioner*

Situation   *Possible roles*

1 A patient comes to your last appointment of the day with a difficult psychological problem, but you specially want to be home in reasonable time that evening	Confidant Gatekeeper Private individual	Clinician Team member Human being
2 A practice meeting is called to consider setting up an open-door stop-smoking clinic. You are to chair the meeting	Team leader/ member Shaper of policy Business person	Authority figure Resource allocator Family physician

---

You will come across many such situations that call simultaneously for different roles that are more or less compatible with each other in practice, just as you will meet a variety of more or less well defined clinical problems. Unless care is taken to stop and think about them, it is easy to be overwhelmed by confusion and uncertainty. Your experience as a registrar is precious because it provides more time to stand back and consider problems and matters of interest than ever you are likely to get later, so take that opportunity.

To do this you need a structure, for without it the moments when a need is perceived will pass, and opportunities for reflection will be lost. Therefore keep a diary or notebook, and enter in it those topics or problems that need further consideration to form an agenda for your self-directed learning. Enter things that you feel you have done well, too, for awareness of the things you are good at will reinforce your strengths, and give you insight into how you work. In turn this will help you to find ways to improve your knowledge and skills in areas that need improvement, and increase awareness of your attitudes to your work which can so easily be taken for granted.

This material can then be used on your own, or in one-to-one tutorials, small groups on day-release courses, or case presentations or critical event audits. Remember that three things are needed for learning in this way:

- Accurate and current knowledge: therefore read the journals and relevant publications
- Awareness of your work: therefore audit yourself at work to see yourself in action
- Reflection on methods and outcomes: therefore take time to think about your working methods and results

Conclusion

When you have learned to see yourself at work, to understand your roles and the expectations of your patients, and to apply the latest in clinical knowledge, you will grow in wisdom and maturity. Passing the MRCGP examination should not then be a problem!

References

Howie JGR, Heaney DJ, Maxwell M et al Quality at general practice consultations: cross-sectional survey. *British Medical Journal*, 1999, 319, 738-43.

Marinker M (Ed) (1990) *Medical Audit in General Practice.* London, British Medical Journal.

RCGP (1972) *The Future General Practitioner — Learning and Teaching.* London, Royal College of General Practitioners.

5   Consulting skills assessment by videotape

Peter Tate

The video examination is the only part of the examination that takes place in your own surgery. It is also the only part over which you have control. You decide which consultations to send to the examiners and which to leave out. You do not need to collect your evidence until you are happy with your consulting ability, and you can check your opinion with a friend, trainer or mentor. This puts considerable responsibility on you to understand clearly the nature of the assessment. It is true to say that many of the candidates who fail this module do so, not because of actual incompetence in consulting, but because they fail to demonstrate their competence within the submitted videotape.

What is expected of you?

First, the plain facts. You will need to construct a selection of seven consultations of up to 15 minutes in length. You must include at least one consultation with a child under 10 years of age, and at least one with a significant social or psychological dimension. These examples of your work must be submitted on a single full size VHS videotape. All the consultations must be in English. You will also be expected to complete the workbook, which includes a consultation assessment form for each consultation you include, and a videotape log to enable the examiners to see at a glance the contents of the tape.

What is the examination looking for?

The assessment is based on the concept of competency, meaning that combination of knowledge, skills, and attitudes which, when applied to a particular situation leads to a given outcome. You might find it helpful to use the analogy of the driving test, in which the competency three-point turn requires you to turn the car to face the opposite direction, using forward and reverse gears safely without endangering other road users or striking the kerbs or other obstacles. The number of forward/reverse manoeuvres is not precisely specified, nor is there a time limit, but the examiner would expect the whole process to be carried out with a certain smoothness. Clearly, this competency includes many skills, such as clutch control, road awareness, steering, etc, but it has a specific, recognisable outcome, namely the car pointing the other way.

Similarly, consulting-skill competencies have been specified. For example, you are required to demonstrate the ability to discover the reasons for a patient's attendance, by eliciting their symptoms, which includes two competencies, first encouraging the patient to 'spill the beans', and second not ignoring cues. We do not specify how the patient is encouraged to give their account of their symptoms: this may be by open questions, appropriate use of silence, or some other way. Nor do we need to specify how the cues are responded to. We do expect that at least some bits of unsolicited information are picked up by the doctor.

As you can see, a competence is a sort of complex skill, the possession of which is demonstrated by achieving the relevant performance criterion. Possession of the competence does not imply that the doctor uses it every time. However, as a candidate, unless you can demonstrate the competence in action, we cannot assume you possess it. You must be clear that the examination is looking for examples of what you can do.

This approach to the assessment of your consulting competence is therefore that you:

- Know which competencies must be demonstrated
- Conform to rules governing the submission of evidence
- Should be guided by a mentor or trainer
- Submit the evidence when it is ready

From your point of view, you must submit to the examiners a videotape with a range of challenge that clearly demonstrates your current consulting ability. You might find it helpful to look on your tape as a portfolio of competence, a collection of effective consultations put together over a period of time.

The standard defined

What is the standard? The answer to this may seem rather complicated at first, but hopefully you will find it quite simple by the time you have begun to collect your work together.

In order to define a standard of consulting competence the examiners drew on their own experience, the world literature and pilot trials of the method. First, a simple and effective way of structuring the definition had to be found.

This was achieved by using the methodology associated with the national vocational qualifications (NVQ). These are essentially workplace oriented and task-based descriptions. Consulting competence was divided into five units:

1 Discover the reasons for a patient's attendance
2 Define the clinical problem(s)
3 Explain the problem(s) to the patient.
4 Address the patient's problem(s)
5 Make effective use of the consultation

Each of these units was subdivided into a variable number of elements. For example in the first unit, 'Discover the reasons for the patient's attendance', there were four elements:

A Elicit the patient's account of the symptom(s) that made him/her turn to the doctor
B Obtain relevant items of social and occupational circumstances
C Explore the patient's health understanding
D Enquire about continuing problems

Even at the element level it was felt that these tasks were too broad to be reliably assessed, so a further and more specific level was defined. These are the performance criteria (PC). Each element of the definition has one or more performance criteria. This structure is shown diagrammatically in figure 5.1 (see page 61).

Figure 5.1   *The structure of the assessment system*

UNIT   .... Element A PC1
                                            PC2

         .... Element B PC1

         .... Element C PC1
                                            PC2
                                            PC3

Five units   Variable numbers of elements and
               performance criteria

The units and elements were derived by an assimilation of the literature relating to clinical and consulting competence appropriate to British general practice. The performance criteria were derived by interrogating examiners who are, of course, all practising general practitioners, challenging them to dissect out those performance tasks which would be required to achieve the higher level elements and units.

The question asked was: What must happen for that to be achieved? Thus the unit 'discover the reasons for the patient's attendance' has four elements, of which one, 'elicit the patient's account of the symptoms which made him/her turn to the doctor' has two performance criteria:

• The doctor encourages the patient's contribution at
  appropriate points in the consultation
• The doctor picks up patient cues.

But another element 'explore the patient's health understanding' has only one performance criterion:

- The doctor takes the patient's health understanding into account

The full range of competencies to be demonstrated comprises five units, which are divided into 16 elements and 21 performance criteria. They are discussed in more detail below

Achieving a pass or a pass with merit

The standard required for the consulting skills assessment by videotape is therefore defined by the performance criteria, and a pass is determined by the answer to the question: Can the candidate do what the performance criteria require? In order to pass you must provide sufficient evidence that you can achieve all the PCs which are identified by the letter (P) (standing for pass); these are shown in the boxes on the following pages.

Sufficient evidence is given by demonstrating each one at least three times. Some skills used in consulting are more complex than these, and, in accordance with the introduction of a merit grade within the exam, candidates who can show these additional skills will be considered for a pass with merit. The additional PCs used to make this assessment are identified by the letter (M) (for merit), and are clearly more patient centred than those required to achieve a bare pass.

Ensuring consistency of judgement

The trouble is, as in all definitions, the words can be interpreted in different ways. How appropriate is appropriate? How much sharing? How effective? And so on. As part of their continuing training the examiners meet regularly to internalise the standard. You, however, do not have that luxury, so how can you judge your own standard? If you are a GP registrar you have the advantage of having an experienced trainer to start with. Record and discuss your consulting at least once a month, but you should not use the MRGP methodology all the time for there are other ways to think about consultations. There is a great richness in the doctor patient consultation, so do look at it from lots of angles. Read about it; there are several good books and dozens of interesting articles on the subject, a selection of which is shown in appendix 1. You will also have a registrar group, in which watching and discussing consultations with your peers can be very helpful, but you will need a skilful group leader. If you are no longer a registrar it may be more difficult. Even so, just recording yourself for a while helps, but ideally a mentor is desirable. There are consultation courses available too.

To help you further understand what is meant by the performance criteria required for pass and merit here is a detailed description of each one.

Detailed guide to the performance criteria

The following paragraphs are set out with the units shown in bold type, and their subsidiary elements and performance criteria which must be demonstrated to pass this module set out in boxes. Each of these PCs is discussed in some detail. There are other PCs mentioned in the workbook, but as these are not assessed in either the MRCGP or MAP procedures they are not discussed here.

UNIT 1   **Discover the reasons for a patient's attendance**

Element A		ELICIT PATIENT'S ACCOUNT OF THE SYMPTOM(S) WHICH MADE HIM/HER TURN TO THE DOCTOR
(P)	PC (1)	the doctor encourages the patient's contribution at appropriate points in the consultation
(P)	PC (2)	the doctor responds to cues

PC1

This PC has the outcome of an adequate account of the presenting problem: it requires you to demonstrate active listening skills; you will not achieve it simply because your patient gives a good account without prompting, as some do. Active listening means showing evidence of attentiveness, not interrupting, reflecting back answers to create follow-up questions, as in: 'What do you mean by dizzy?'

There should be evidence that the doctor can encourage a contribution from a patient who needs to be encouraged.

PC 2

A cue is a sign made by the patient, whether consciously or not, that is capable of being perceived by the doctor. Not every consultation contains cues that need a response. However, since responding to cues about the nature of the problem is regarded by the examiners as a core competency, it is up you to demonstrate some in your selection of consultations.

Verbal cues may be simply what is said, some may be what is not said and may be related to the tone of voice, facial expression, posture or actions of patient. An example of response to a non-verbal cue would be a visibly sad patient, to whom you comment: 'You seem rather low'. A verbal cue might be the patient saying: 'It's my back again'. If you not only addressed the present episode but also explored the previous ones, you would have responded to the cue given by the word 'again'.

Reflection can be a response to a cue. The patient might say, 'And I've felt low this week', and the doctor reply, 'Low?'. Equally, the same cue could be responded to by a later statement by the doctor: 'You mentioned earlier that you felt low. Could you expand on that?'

Element	B	OBTAIN RELEVANT ITEMS OF SOCIAL AND OCCUPATIONAL CIRCUMSTANCES
(P)	PC	the doctor elicits appropriate details to place the complaint(s) in a social and psychological context

It can be argued that every problem has social and psychological elements, yet the failure to explore these is a common cause of failure in this module. To demonstrate it effectively choose a consultation where the patient is not well known to you and where you need to elicit the background information in a natural way.

Occupational may mean the patient's job, but could equally be how they fill their day, and crucially how the complaint (symptom, illness) impacts on this. There may also be the reverse situation in which occupation could be affecting health. The relevance of the psychological dimension is most obvious where the patient is experiencing significant emotional distress. If the examiner is content that the context (nature of the problem, and the patient's manner) suggests this is not the case, then you will demonstrate competence simply by exploring the social and occupational factors without exploring feelings if, indeed, they are not appropriate.

However, this PC is not simply 'psychological and social', but rather the appropriate exploration of these areas for relevant items given the presenting problem. Asking, 'So what do you do for a living?', while the prescription is being printed is unlikely to be an appropriate or a timely exploration.

Element	C	EXPLORE THE PATIENT'S HEALTH UNDERSTANDING
(M)	PC	the doctor takes the patient's health understanding into account

This is a merit-level PC and is overtly patient centred. Remember that it sits in the area of 'discovering the reasons for attendance'. It is most simply addressed by asking, once you have heard the patient's story, 'What do you think it could be?' There are few situations where such a question, properly and sensitively asked, is not appropriate. (The obvious exception would be when the patient has already told you, as: 'I cut my finger this morning while opening a can of beans'!)

In a patient with headaches you may ask: 'You have had these headaches for a few weeks now, and I was wondering whether you had any ideas yourself as to what it might be due to?' This invites the patient to discuss their health understanding with the doctor, indicating that the doctor is interested and concerned about the patient's understanding of their symptoms. It is quite likely that an open question such as, 'So how are these headaches affecting you? You look very worried', might elicit a response that satisfies more than one criterion, such as picking up cues, exploring psychosocial issues or eliciting health understanding.

Element C refers to 'exploring', since you cannot take the patient's health understanding into account until you have discovered what it is. A patient who asks: 'Do you think it's an allergy, doctor?' has some understanding or misunderstanding of allergies which could be explored by asking: 'What makes you think it might be?' Implicit in this is the belief that patients' ideas are intrinsically valid and valuable in understanding the nature of their problem.

UNIT 2   Define the clinical problem(s)

Element A	OBTAIN ADDITIONAL INFORMATION ABOUT SYMPTOMS AND DETAILS OF MEDICAL HISTORY
(P) PC	the doctor obtains sufficient information for no serious condition to be missed

This is the 'medical safety' PC, which addresses the focused enquiry that commonly occurs during the consultation, though not necessarily at a particular stage: it may happen during an examination, or later, during the explanation, or even as an afterthought. It is about taking a history in the degree of detail which is compatible with safety, but which takes account of the epidemiological realities of general practice.

The PC requires you to recognise, from what has been said, any potentially serious diagnostic possibilities that an average general practitioner should consider. These would typically include suicidal thoughts in a patient with depression, malignancy in a patient with chronic cough, change in bowel habit, dysphagia, or weight loss, and so on. Competence may be demonstrated by asking focused, closed questions, such as, 'Have you noticed any blood in the stool (sputum, urine)?', or an appropriate suicide question.

Serious need not mean life-threatening. A child with a cough or otitis media should probably be asked about asthma symptoms, or about their hearing. A person with back ache should, unless it is manifestly trivial, be asked about red flag symptoms.

Essentially, PC1 looks for medical competence in history taking. It may legitimately be absent when the presenting complaint is very minor. This is one reason why you are advised not to include many minor problems among your consultations.

Element B		ASSESS THE CONDITION OF THE PATIENT BY APPROPRIATE PHYSICAL OR MENTAL EXAMINATION
(P)	PC	the doctor chooses an examination which is likely to confirm or disprove hypotheses which could reasonably have been formed, OR to address a patient's concern

This is not about competence in performing the examination, which cannot usually be judged on tape, but about the appropriateness of the examination in relation to the hypothesis. The examiner will be thinking: Why has the candidate chosen to do that examination? Sometimes you may say something to the patient that gives a clue to the hypothesis: 'I am just going to look in your ears to see if there is wax there'. But more often the reason has to be inferred from the context.

The element specifies appropriate physical or mental examination, and we accept as evidence of mental examination any reasonable attempt at assessing mental state, where appropriate. Exploring suicidal intention would be a necessary part in a depressed patient seen for the first time, but perhaps not at follow-up; so would formal examination of thought disorder in a possibly psychotic patient, and memory testing in one with possible dementia.

Element   C   MAKE A WORKING DIAGNOSIS
(P)   PC   the doctor appears to make a clinically
                      appropriate working diagnosis

Your diagnosis may be explicit and declared to the patient, but more often the examiners will infer it from your explanation and management plan. Please make sure that you enter your working diagnosis in each consultation summary form in the workbook.

UNIT 3   Explain the problem(s) to the patient

Element   A   SHARE THE FINDINGS WITH THE
                      PATIENT
(P)   PC   the doctor explains the diagnosis,
                      management and effects of treatment

These three things should be explained, although sometimes the effects of treatment (eg improve the symptoms) might not need to be stated. There must be evidence of an explanation of the patient's problem. The element states that the findings should be shared with the patient. A short explanation may be enough but it must be relevant, understandable and appropriate.

Element   B   TAILOR THE EXPLANATION TO
                      THE PATIENT
(P)   PC (1)   the doctor explains in language
                      appropriate to the patient
(M)   PC (2)   the doctor's explanation takes account
                      of some or all of the patient's elicited
                      beliefs

PC1

You should avoid medical jargon and use words which your patient is likely to understand. Remember that words can have different, even opposite, meanings for doctor and patient. A patient whose leg is hurting 'something chronic' probably has an acute rather than a chronic pain. Beware of abbreviations (MSU, ECG). If your patient asks for clarification, it is probably best not to choose that consultation for the examination.

PC2

Clearly this depends on the health beliefs having been elicited in element C of unit 1 and so it is also a merit PC. The competence can be identified as a reference back to some idea which was expressed by the patient, and which the doctor is addressing, either to affirm, to modify, or to refute. Thus, 'So your irritable bowel syndrome is very likely to be related to the stress you were telling me about earlier'; or having elicited the belief that a rash was an allergy to certain foods, 'This rash is called psoriasis, and is caused by over-active cells in the skin, but it is probably not affected by what you eat'.

This criterion cannot be satisfied without having previously identified the patient's health beliefs and is the most patient centred of all the criteria, as it requires true involvement in the patient's narrative.

Element	C	ENSURE THAT THE EXPLANATION IS UNDERSTOOD AND ACCEPTED BY THE PATIENT
(M)	PC	the doctor seeks to confirm the patient's understanding

Having given an explanation, it is appropriate, and effective, to check understanding, so it may be surprising that this is a merit PC. However, most candidates do not check for understanding! It clearly implies the use of a question — 'Does that make sense?', 'Have I made that clear?', 'Tell me what you understand by that?' Or, 'What does the term angina mean to you?'. A dialogue between the patient and yourself ensuring that the explanation is understood and accepted, would satisfy this PC.

More problematic is the cursory 'Okay?'. It depends what happens next. If the patient appears to take this as a check of understanding, by responding, it will probably do, but there is a risk that patients will say 'yes' to such a query, because it is far easier to say yes than no! Many doctors add 'okay?' to all their explanations, as a routine, without expecting an answer. The context should determine whether there is a real 'seeking to confirm understanding'.

UNIT 4   Address the patient's problem(s)

Element A of this unit is not discussed here because it does not need to be demonstrated to pass, though it is a valuable quality and may be found in the workbook.

Element	B	CHOOSE AN APPROPRIATE FORM OF MANAGEMENT
(P)	PC	the doctor's management plan is appropriate for the working diagnosis, reflecting a good understanding of modern accepted medical practice

This does not depend on the working diagnosis being right — it simply relates the management plan to the working diagnosis, and to modern accepted medical practice. (In the era of evidence-based medicine, we must read that as modern accepted and, when possible, evidence-based, medical practice.)

The standard here is what a consensus of MRCGP examiners would reach, with allowance for alternative approaches. Thus, depression can be managed in various ways such as by prescribing antidepressants, arranging cognitive therapy, using a problem-solving strategy, referral to a specialist resource or, in mild cases, by support and careful follow-up by the GP.

Element	C	INVOLVE THE PATIENT IN THE MANAGEMENT PLAN TO THE APPROPRIATE EXTENT
(P)	PC	the doctor's shares management options with the patient

This is the most patient-centred of the non-merit criteria, and also perhaps the most crucial for you as a candidate, since failure to demonstrate competence in this area has been the single most common cause of failing the module. Since sharing options may not be a common behaviour, it becomes an important factor in deciding which consultations to submit.

The extent of sharing will vary according to the context ('to the appropriate extent'). This will depend on the patient, how capable they are of engaging in such involvement, the problem and what sort of options exist. Thus a retired science teacher with newly diagnosed hypertension might expect (or need) to be involved very substantially in a range of options, from lifestyle modification, through choice of drugs, to frequency and nature of follow-up. On the other hand, a learning disabled teenager with severe tonsillitis might not appreciate a discussion of whether to take penicillin for five or 10 days, and a simple consideration of whether to use tablets or liquid would be more appropriate.

Sharing management options might include treatment alternatives, referral options, choices of when or whether to review a patient, whether or when a patient should return to work after a period of illness, but it must demonstrate your ability to involve the patient in the options that are available. For example, the case of a patient with tension headache might include a discussion of treatments available, eg analgesics, relaxation techniques, referral for stress counselling etc, or could involve a discussion of the alternative possibilities for follow up. Simply saying, 'I am going to refer you to a stress counsellor, is that all right?', is not an example of sharing. For all but the most self-confident patients, this is a statement of your intention and not an invitation to discuss options. However a consultation that contains the words options, choices, or alternatives and involves the patient in a two-way dialogue should fulfil this criterion.

The underlying idea of this PC is shared decision-making, whether this is about medication, referral, investigations, or time off work.

UNIT 5   **Make effective use of the consultation**

Element	A	MAKE EFFICIENT USE OF RESOURCES
(P)	PC	the doctor's prescribing behaviour is appropriate

The word appropriate implies a judgement against the examiner's norms, and by extension, the consensus of the Panel of Examiners, in deciding what, in the circumstances of this consultation, would be appropriate prescribing.

Deliberate non-prescribing, particularly of antibiotics, can be appropriate behaviour here, as can advice to purchase over-the-counter medicines. There will be cases, however, where a decision about prescribing does not arise, as where the consultation is about a surgical condition (eg a hernia) and the plan is to refer, or where the problem is social (eg housing), and the plan is to take some administrative action. The competence is simply not demonstrable in such consultations. But remember that in order to pass, you do not need to demonstrate competence in all PCs in all consultations; three out five is the current rule.

This criterion requires evidence of the development of a sympathetic relationship between doctor and patient, being mutually responsive to each others' signals. This is something that develops during the

Element	B	ESTABLISH A RELATIONSHIP WITH THE PATIENT
(P)	PC	the patient and the doctor appear to have established a rapport

consultation as the doctor shows awareness of the patient's cues, understands what the patient is communicating and ensures that the patient understands and is involved in the care. Examiners judge rapport by both verbal and non-verbal signals.

Preparing the videotape

When you apply for the examination you will be sent the workbook which includes detailed instructions for preparing the recording, obtaining consent and the conduct of consultations during the recording. I will highlight some of the issues here.

Preparing for the recording

Remember that the final product must be a full size VHS videotape, recorded at normal not slow speed, and in normal format ie not super VHS. The tape is yours to provide, so it makes sense to buy one of the super high quality/professional varieties as this improves the picture and sound quality, especially of re-recorded consultations. You need to send only seven consultations, your five preferred ones and two more. It is very sensible, probably essential, to make a copy. Tapes can get broken, chewed up by vicious machines or lost, even in the best-regulated circles. Often you will find a hospital audio-visual department will help with copying facilities. Local course organisers are usually informed on what is available. In desperation, your local high street photography store can often help, at a price, but beware of confidentiality.

The camera

Most cameras these days are no longer the large VHS type but come in a variety of formats, including digital. This is to your advantage as the quality of these images when re-recorded onto VHS tape is excellent, and much better than dubbing VHS to VHS. Most cameras have a reasonable wide-angle lens, though if not such a lens is usually easy to purchase and not dear. The microphones on new cameras tend to be good enough in small well sound-proofed surgeries with the window closed. If your surgery is next to the M1 with paper-thin walls, it is wise to connect a desk microphone. It is worth reminding you that the quality of the image and sound is entirely your responsibility. Poor sound and vision make it difficult for the examiners to recognise your abilities, and if they cannot do so they may not give you the benefit of the doubt. Very bad sound and/or vision will be rejected. The commonest sound fault is the now ubiquitous printer, which cuts out all conversation often at a crucial juncture. Two or three children all talking at once while mum weeps and mumbles can also be very difficult to assess.

Lighting and siting

The commonest visual fault is backlighting. If you are sitting in front of a window or strong light the camera iris shuts down and you and your patient become silhouettes with no visible features. To avoid this some cameras will compensate if you can find the right button, but if that fails move the light and draw the curtains. Another major fault is not seeing enough of your patient. Ideally, you should both be in clear view, but if this is really difficult make sure it is the patient who is in view. Some practice, with a little trial and error, is essential. All the more reason to get into the habit of recording and reviewing regularly.

Consent

The RCGP will provide a mastercopy of the required consent form, and you should make as many copies of this as you need. At the time of writing we will also accept the form approved for summative assessment. The form requires signed consent both before and after the encounter. Remember these forms last only for one year; forms that have expired cannot be accepted.

There is sometimes a problem with patient consent, which is that candidates have experienced frustration because patients often refuse consent for those very consultations which most clearly demonstrate their consulting abilities. This has been noted by some to be mainly in the area of psychological and sexual problems. It has to be said, however, that most candidates have not reported such difficulties. There are several possible solutions to this difficult problem.

- Arrange video recorded surgeries well in advance so that patients are aware at the time of booking the appointment that recordings are to be made
- Look at the way your practice handles the consent issue. The

attitude of the receptionists can be crucial. Involve them and explain what you are doing and why. If you can 'sell' it to your receptionists there is a greater chance you can sell it to your patients. This applies to some extent with partners too
• Persuade your trainer, partners and practice manager to create a poster for display in the waiting room, or do so yourself with their consent. This can proclaim the positive reasons for recording and the confidentiality associated with it
• It may be an issue to bring up with a patient participation group should your practice have one
• An article in the practice newsletter could be helpful.

Conduct during recording

Do behave ethically at all times. To help with this, clear guidelines are included with the instructions for preparing the videotape, which you will receive on application for this module. Physical examinations of an intimate or sensitive nature must be held out of sight of the camera, but unless the examination takes place in another room you should leave the camera running so that your voices can be heard. Often the simplest way of handling the recording of an intimate examination is to place the lens cap over the lens, but don't forget to take it off again.

It takes a few trial runs for most of us to feel and look natural in front of a camera. Some always feel uneasy. Two suggestions may be helpful here. One is obvious: the more often you do it the easier it becomes. The other is less obvious: try imagining the camera is switched on even when it is not. If you do this regularly self-consciousness diminishes and self-analysis increases.

Selecting and editing

It takes hardly any time to record consultations but a lot of time to watch them. Your ability may already be obvious enough for you to record a surgery or two and to submit it unedited. The fellowship by assessment process expects this sort of approach, but for most MRCGP candidates it will be necessary to select and edit, not least because otherwise your case mix may just be a series of sore throats and bad ears. Such a series is unlikely to give the examiners enough material to judge your overall competence.

There is a tricky balance to be struck here. Examiners do not want you to spend days searching for absolute consulting perfection to the detriment of all else. Perfection is rare, if it exists at all, but competence should be usual. Therefore, try to select a mix of presentations. A new presentation plus the follow-up may very clearly demonstrate a wider range of your behaviours than a single consultation.

Remember not to include consultations longer than 15 minutes because they will not be watched. This does not mean that long consultations are unimportant, but does mean that examiners wish to see samples of your work in which you are working at a speed that reflects the reality of day-to-day general practice. It follows that very short encounters are also unlikely to demonstrate many performance criteria to the level expected. A range consultations lasting eight to 15 minutes seems sensible.

It is unwise to send in glaring errors of any sort. We all have ineffective consultations, even downright awful ones, but it is common sense not to send these in to be assessed. If you wish to wear the hair shirt please do so with your trainer, not with the examiners. This assessment is about showing us what you can do and demonstrating your basic consulting competence. We do not wish to see your occasional incompetence.

Making your own assessment

It is beyond the scope of this chapter to teach consulting, but to help you reflect upon your work in a way that is relevant to the exam. Figure 5.2 (see page 77) shows a checklist or critique you can use to review your consultations yourself. It is not unlike those used by the examiners.

You will find it useful to identify first those areas which you felt you did well, and then the areas where you felt you could have done better. If there is a lot in the first column and nothing too drastic in the second then that looks like a consultation worth including. This critique form can help you further to complete a passing portfolio. The examiners require at least three examples of each PC out of five

Figure 5.2   A consultation critique sheet

In the areas listed below, what was done well?
Could anything be improved?

Items of competence	Well done	Not so good	Improvement
• Discover the reasons for a patient's attendance • Elicit the patient's account of the symptoms			
• Encourage the patient's contribution • Observe and use cues • Obtain relevant items of social & occupational circumstances			
• Explore patient's health understanding • Define the clinical problems • Explain problems to patient • Explain diagnosis, management & effects of treatment			
• Use appropriate language • Use patient's health understanding • Check patient's understanding of explanation • Manage patient's problem			
• Ensure plan appropriate for working diagnosis • Share management options • Effective use of consultation			
• Use time appropriately • Prescribe appropriately • Develop and use your relationship • Opportunistic health advice			

NB This list includes some items of competence other than those
needed to pass the consulting skills module

consultations, so by using such a form you may see, for instance, that although one consultation does not demonstrate the prescribing PC everything else is present. It would then be wise to make sure at least three other consultations do contain the prescribing PC. You should perform this exercise for all the PCs. The rule of thumb is three out of five, four out of seven.

Completing the workbook

When you have selected and recorded your consultations on to the tape you are going to submit for examination, it is time to fill in the videotape log situated at the beginning of the workbook. This section is to help the examiners select and move about your evidence and, like the rest of the workbook, it is in your own interest to fill it in legibly and correctly. The examiners use recorders that count in real time, minute by minute, but if your machine does not do this don't panic, use a watch. The log requires you to record the length of time that has elapsed from the start of the tape until the beginning of each consultation. This of course means that the previous requirement to have a date and time stamp on the camera is no longer necessary.

The main reason for the patient consulting should be defined in general practice terms in enough detail to give the examiners a flavour of its content. The other details are self-explanatory.

You will need to fill in an assessment form, shown in figure 5.3 (see page 79) for every consultation, though you don't have to wait to the editing stage to do so. It is worth keeping some of these forms to hand during consultations to help in your editing and selecting, enabling you to keep the details fresh in your mind. This will help when selecting the material to submit.

There are some points to make about this form.

- 'Working diagnosis' means the hypothesis on which your actions are based, eg: presenting complaint: 'tired all the time'. Working diagnosis: depressive illness with social cause and consequences

- Be punctilious in giving information about the outcomes of consultations and prescriptions issued. Often the videotape evidence is not clear in these areas, and without this crucial information the examiners cannot make a fair assessment of these areas.

You will need to outline the setting of the consultation, what you achieved and what you feel may arise later. All this briefly please, no more than 50 words.

All this does take time, but it will be easier if you fill in the consultation assessment forms using photocopies from the workbook as you go along, and if some of your selection is done with your trainer at normal tutorials. You are required to send only seven consultations so you should not find the task too onerous.

Figure 5.3   *Consultation assessment form as used in the workbook*

Reference number:

Presenting complaint(s):

Relevant background information:
(eg *previous knowledge of or consultation with this patient*)

Working diagnosis:

Outcomes of the consultation:
(eg *referral, no action, certificate, review*)

Prescription:
(*provide full details of any prescription given or test ordered, with justification*)

In approximately 50 words outline the setting of the consultation, what was achieved, and what issues may arise later.

Don't use the workbook to try to explain away dubious behaviour, it is better not to send such consultations. Remember we are looking for 'can do'.

How is your videotape assessed?

Your tape and workbook will be assessed by a group of trained examiners who are, by definition, working general practitioners with several years experience. The examiners will begin by watching the first five consultations on your tape. Each of the five consultations is watched by a separate examiner, working alone.

The examiners report their findings to a coordinating examiner. If satisfactory evidence of your competence in all pass-level performance criteria has been found on at least three occasions somewhere in the first five consultations you can be sure that your tape will pass.

We understand that not every consultation will give you the scope to demonstrate all the pass PCs to the required level. Moreover, at the discretion of the consulting skills convenor and the convenor of the panel two rather than three demonstrations of competence may suffice for some PCs, but you would be wiser to aim to satisfy each PC three times in the first five consultations.

If we do not find sufficient evidence in the first five consultations, your remaining two will be assessed. In this case four demonstrations of competence in each pass level PC may be required to pass. It is as fair as we can make it. As you can see selection is all. It is probably true that many who do not pass the examination have the ability but simply have not demonstrated that ability in the consultations they chose to submit.

If you are submitting a tape of more than seven consultations — one for summative assessment purposes, perhaps — you must ensure that those for the MRCGP are the first seven on the tape. Under no circumstances will any subsequent consultations be considered.

If, unfortunately, you do fail you will receive feedback on the reasons for failure couched in the terms of the performance criteria.

For instance, it might be that the examiners thought that you regularly ignored patient cues and failed to elicit social and psychological details from your patients. This may look a bit direct and does not describe the good points first as might be preferred, but we hope that at least it will give you something to work on to improve and be successful next time.

Results of the video assessment

Over 3000 candidates have been assessed by this methodology to date. Most of the assessment was done by groups of examiners at residential meetings, which allow discussion and training. The reliability has been found to be very high. The failure rate of the component is about 25%, but many candidates fail the exam overall on the video component alone, having passed written and oral components.

Although some failures were due to lack of evidence of competence in only one performance criterion, most were because competence was not demonstrated in two or more. Remember, a pass is achieved by three demonstrations of competence each of the twelve PCs.

The PCs which candidates most often fail to demonstrate are shown in table 5.1 (see page 82) in descending order.

Overall the examiners have been pleased with the general standard, but a patient-centred approach to consulting has been less in evidence than might have been anticipated. The current merit rate is 20%. To encourage you to achieve a merit by showing a patient-centred approach table 5.2 (see page 82) gives a reminder of the three PCs which you need to demonstrate to do so.

Summary

This is a part of the examination that no one should fail. Read and understand the criteria. When you believe you have reached the standard required check with your trainer or mentor, make your final tape and send us the evidence. Hopefully, the examiners will agree with your own judgement. The kind of consulting the RCGP wishes to encourage involves sharing, observing, eliciting, relating and managing effectively. Go and do it.

A list of suggestions for further reading is given in appendix 1.

Table 5.1   *The PC which are most commonly absent in submitted evidence*

(in descending order of frequency)

The doctor shares management options with the patient
The doctors elicits appropriate details to place the complaint
in a social and psychological context
The doctor responds to cues
The doctor's management plan is appropriate for the
working diagnosis
The doctor explains the diagnosis, management and effects
of treatment
The doctor explains in language appropriate to the patient

Table 5.2   *The three PCs which are needed to pass with merit*

Unit 1, element C
        (M) PC   The doctor takes the patient's health
                  understanding into account

Unit 3, element B
        (M) PC   The doctor's explanation takes account of
                  some or all of the patient's elicited health
                  beliefs

Unit 3, element C
        (M) PC   The doctor seeks to confirm the patient's
                  understanding

---

6 Consulting skills assessment by the simulated surgery

Peter Burrows

The simulated surgery is an alternative consulting skills component of the MRCGP that is available to candidates who are unable to submit a videotape of their consultations. It has been developed from the objective structured clinical examination (OSCE) which many doctors will be familiar with as a format for undergraduate examinations.

However, whereas in the OSCE the candidate rotates around a number of stations undertaking clinical or other tasks at each one, in the simulated surgery the candidate stays in a 'consulting room' and is visited by a number of patients just like in a normal surgery in general practice. The patients are role-players who have been trained to present a particular case and will behave in a standardised manner to each candidate. The consultations can last up to 10 minutes, but no longer, and 20 cases are presented in two sessions of 10 in the morning and afternoon.

This method of assessing consulting skills has been developed in parallel with the video assessment system. Though the processes and terminology used seem very different the two systems are designed to measure similar attributes to an equivalent standard. Experience has shown that their performances are highly comparable.

Who is eligible?

Candidates wishing to take the simulated surgery instead of the video assessment as their consulting skills component must present valid reasons to the examination department as to why they cannot provide a videotape of their clinical work. This might be for any of the following reasons:

- Because they are not currently working in general practice
- They are working locum sessions and are unable to use a video-camera in the practice
- They do not customarily consult in English
- They or a large proportion of their patients have religious or cultural objections to the recording of their consultations.

Applications to take the simulated surgery must be supported by a member or Fellow of the RCGP who is asked to confirm that the candidate would have insuperable difficulties in providing a videotape. The availability of the simulated surgery is limited at the present time, and candidates are admitted on a first-come, first-served basis. Those for whom there is no place available at a given session will get priority for the next session and their time limit for passing the exam overall will be correspondingly extended if necessary.

How is it organised?

If your application is accepted you will be given date and place to attend. For the convenience of candidates coming from other countries who also wish to take the orals, the timing will enable you to do so on the same visit to the UK. You should expect to attend for a full day; coffee, lunch and tea will be provided. You should bring your diagnostic kit, eg stethoscope, sphygmomanometer, opth/auriscope, pen-torch and disposable tongue depressors, peak flow meter and patella hammer. There is no need to bring gloves, speculae or urinalysis kit.

On arrival you will be made welcome and told about the housekeeping arrangements. The rules and procedure for the surgery will be explained and you will have the opportunity to ask questions. You will be shown to a simulated consulting room, which contains a table and chairs which you may arrange according to your preferred consulting style. There will be an examination couch available either in your room or in an adjacent examination room. There will also be a chair for the examiner which should be placed out of your direct line of vision. On the table you will find pads of prescription and certificate forms, an appointment list for your surgery, and records of the patients whom you will see. During the surgery you should stay in the room and you should not attempt to talk to other candidates.

Tea or coffee will be brought to you during the breaks. Lunch is served between the morning and afternoon surgeries, and you can, of course, socialise with your fellow candidates during this time. You should inform the exam department in advance of any special dietary requirements.

What happens during the surgery?

Starting the consultation

A bell will be rung, or whistle blown, to signal the start of the consultation. The patient will enter your room in role and should be treated as a new patient whom you have not met before. Greet them by name and show them to the chair. The patient will tell you why they have come, and you should respond as you would normally, so that a natural consultation ensues. The examiner will enter the room after the patient, only to observe; he or she takes no part in the consultation and you should act as if they were not there.

Physical examination

This should be done if you consider it appropriate to the case. There will be no actual physical signs present, but you should examine the patient in such a way that you would find them if they were present. You will be marked on your technique and courtesy. If you wish to undertake an intimate examination you should ask the patient, but don't persist if the patient declines. In such a case you may assume that the findings would be negative. Occasionally, you will be given a card with a picture or description of the examination findings on it. Treat this as if you had discovered these findings by your own examination.

Ending the consultation

If the consultation comes to a natural end within the 10 minutes allowed, the patient will get up and leave, followed by the examiner. At the end of the 10 minutes a bell will be rung and you should finish your consultation at that point. You will not be marked for anything which happens after the bell. The examiners recognise that this time constraint is artificial but it is the same for every candidate.

Efficient use of time is a component of competence in general practice, and the cases are written so that the essential tasks of each consultation can be completed within 10 minutes. There is a short break of about two minutes between cases to allow the examiners to record their marks and the role players to prepare themselves for the next consultation. You may meet the same role-players in different roles in the afternoon; if so, please do not assume any previous acquaintance with the patient.

Case notes

The purpose of these is to provide you with some information about the patient, such as their name, age, sex and background history. The details are deliberately kept to a minimum to avoid distracting you into following irrelevant leads

However, the notes may contain important information about prior events, eg a consultation with a colleague or the practice nurse, some test or x-ray results, or a letter from a hospital consultant or another practitioner. You are advised to read them before the patient comes in so that you are well briefed about the background to the consultation. You may write in the notes if you wish for authenticity, but your records will not be marked by the examiner.

Prescriptions, certificates, etc

These should be made out on the stationary provided and given to the patient if appropriate. You will be marked on what you have written. Investigation requests or referral notes which you wish to give to the patient, may be written on the reverse side of the prescriptions, or you may simply tell the patient that you will arrange them later. In this case please ensure that you state what tests you are arranging.

There is no need to mime the giving of information leaflets, diet sheets, etc. Instead, you should tell the patient that they can be collected at the reception desk.

What kind of case can you expect in a simulated surgery?

The answer, broadly speaking, is almost anything that you might encounter in general practice in the UK. A wide range of patients and conditions will be presented:

- The patients in a simulated surgery can be of any age, sex, social class, ethnic origin, occupation or level of ability, although there are some limitations to what can be simulated, eg:
  — small children, though parents may consult on their behalf
  — those with fixed physical signs, though cards and pictures can be used to show these
  — those whom the doctor has encountered previously, though the notes can provide previous history

- The cases in a simulated surgery are selected to provide a range of consultation challenges and can be as varied as any seen in general practice. They may present in the context of:
  — emergency, acute, chronic, preventive or service requests
  — physical, psychological or social problems
  — routine conditions commonly encountered in general practice, or less common conditions that are important to recognise because they may be life-threatening

An example of the kind of case that you might expect to encounter is given in figure 6.1 (see page 88) which shows the briefing the role player will receive. The information for the candidate presented in the medical records is shown in figure 6.2 (see page 89).

Imagine yourself waiting in your surgery for this patient to come from the waiting room; as you wait you remind yourself about him from the records. Also imagine the patient, and how he might present himself with the history given to the role player. Then imagine the consultation that might ensue, and how you would handle it.

This is just the kind of situation that might arise in everyday general practice, and the examiners will be observing how you manage the case presented as though it were a real case. They will be analysing

Figure 6.1   *An example case (a) Role player briefing*

Topic of case: Simple back injury
Patient's name: Jeremy Carter
Age: 20
Sex: Male

Briefing
You are a 20-year-old male, generally fit and healthy, who works as a van delivery driver. You play football for a local team and go to weight training in a gym two or three times a week. Three days ago you did a lift which hurt your back. You wrenched it as you dropped the weight. The pain has not settled yet and this is beginning to worry you. Start by telling the doctor about your problem.

When you are examined
The pain is in the mid lumbar region, and catches you unexpectedly when you lean forward. Your back movements are stiff, and you find it difficult to bend forward. Tilting sideways and leaning backwards are less painful, but you are hesitant to do this, because you think that the pain will catch you again. The pain goes across the back on both sides. The pain does not extend down your legs, and you have no numbness or weakness. There is no impairment of any other function. If the doctor lifts either leg with the knee straight, there is no additional pain in the back or leg.

If the doctor asks
You are stiff after sitting, and although lying down eases the pain somewhat, it returns when you get up. It seems better once you have been moving about for a while. You are becoming concerned that you may have done something serious to your back. You have heard about slipped disc, and wonder whether this is what you have.

You have taken 'a few' paracetamol tablets which helped for a short while. However you don't like taking tablets, and you are becoming rather impatient with the pain. You would really like something to be done quickly for your back, but will accept reassurance that it is likely to settle down on its own. You wonder if it needs to be x-rayed.

You have not previously hurt your back. You have been off work since the incident occurred and you are worried as to how long it will be before you can go back. There is a league football game in 10 days, and you would like to be fit for it.

Figure 6.2   *An example case (b) Records for the candidate*

Name	Jeremy CARTER
Age	20
Occupation	Delivery van driver
3 years ago	Acne moderately severe on forehead
	Oxytet 250 mg, ii bd, 120
Last year	Sprained right ankle playing football
	No evidence of bony injury. Swollen
	around lateral malleolus
	Advice — apply cooling, elevate leg. Then
	tubular bandage and rest.
	Mobilise gradually. No sport for 2-3
	weeks
Since then	No significant illnesses

---

your management using a method devised for the MRCGP simulated surgery, and assessing your performance with a standard marking schedule which has features specific to each case.

What are the examiners looking for?

Although you need a basic knowledge of clinical medicine to pass this component of the MRCGP, the examiners are primarily looking for competence in consulting skills. The method used examines five principal domains of consulting skills. These are shown in figure 6.3 (see page 91).

How are the marks awarded and pass/fail decisions reached?

Most of the domains of consulting skills will be sampled within each case, although some of the cases are written to test a particular skill, and the marks will be correspondingly weighted towards this area. Each case has a marking schedule with five items covering the key features of the case. These are the core tasks which any competent GP should undertake in the context of the particular presentation by the patient. They may correspond to the five domains shown in figure 6.3, but sometimes a domain is represented more than once, or not at all, depending on the nature of the case. The candidate's performance on each item is graded by the examiner as good, satisfactory, barely adequate, not very good or unsatisfactory.

Other aspects of the consultation are not marked even though they may be included or omitted by the candidate. The marking schedule used for the example case of Jeremy Carter is shown in figure 6.4 (see page 92).

Scores

The grades awarded by the examiner for each item are transformed into numerical values and summed to produce a case score. The pass mark is set for each sitting of the examination by the contrasting groups method. The examiners make independent judgements about the grades achieved by a group of candidates whose marks are distributed around the anticipated pass/fail level.

Their scores are then plotted against the number of examiners who judge they have passed. A smooth correlation line is drawn, and the point on the line where half of the examiners would pass a candidate is taken to be the passmark for that sitting. This method allows the passmark to vary according to the examiners' perception of the difficulty of cases chosen on different occasions.

Blueprinting and reliability

Surgeries are compiled according to a blueprint using cases from a case bank. This ensures similar coverage from one sitting of the examination to the next. Examiners undergo training with videotapes of the case to calibrate their judgement. The marking schedule contains anchor statements defining what is good and unsatisfactory performance on each item. Statistical analysis is carried out after each sitting of the exam to check how well the cases have worked. The alpha coefficient of reliability of a recent simulated surgery was 0.85, suggesting a high level of internal consistency between the cases.

Figure 6.3   *The five domains of consulting skills in the simulated surgery assessment*

Data gathering

Interview and history taking, which should be focused and relevant to the complaint

History sufficient to reach a diagnosis and exclude serious possibilities

Physical examination with courtesy and efficiency

Use of information from the records

Establishing rapport, listening and facilitation

Establishing rapport, listening and facilitation

Sensitivity, empathy,

Awareness of the patient's concerns, safety netting

Ethical approach, respect for confidentiality, autonomy, primacy of patient's interests

Communication

Use of verbal and non-verbal skills

Explanation of symptoms and diagnosis

Breaking bad news

Negotiation of treatment

Management

Appropriate and safe treatment, including investigations, prescribing and referral where indicated

Good use of time and resources

Offering options where appropriate

Anticipatory care

Awareness of implications for patient and others

Follow-up arrangements

Health promotion and preventive care

Figure 6.4   *An example case (c) Marking schedule*

NAME   Jeremy Carter   EXAMINER _____

CASE NO _____ STATION _____   CANDIDATE NO ____

1   Information Gathering — interview/history taking   [ ]
    Good Candidate elicits a full history of the injury and subsequent
    progress, with appropriate direct questions about factors making it
    better or worse
    Unsatisfactory Candidate does not elicit a clear history, and does
    not use questions effectively

2   Doctor/Patient Interaction — patient's concerns   [ ]
    Good Candidate is aware of his occupation and sports interest
    and discovers his concern about the effects of the injury and possibility
    of a slipped disc.
    Unsatisfactory Candidate makes no reference to the above and is not
    aware of patient's concerns

3   Information Gathering — physical examination   [ ]
    Good Candidate performs an efficient, structured examination of the
    patient, including observation of back movements, straight leg raising
    and reflexes
    Unsatisfactory Candidate does not examine the patient

4   Communication — explanation   [ ]
    Good Candidate explains likely to be simple injury with no long-term
    consequences, probable recovery within a week, no need for x-rays.
    Unsatisfactory No explanation or grossly wrong explanation of
    diagnosis and likely outcome

5   Management — options   [ ]
    Good Management should include reassurance, appropriate advice on
    activity and work, simple analgesia, possible referral for physiotherapy
    if it doesn't settle
    Unsatisfactory Candidate offers patient no management options, or
    grossly inappropriate ones

Enter one of the following grades in each box:

g — good s — satisfactory b — barely adequate n — not very good
u — unsatisfactory

How should you prepare?

Consulting skills develop with experience, self-awareness, feedback from others and review of your own performance.

Experience

If you are not working regularly in general practice, you should seek opportunities to practise your skills, preferably in the context of British general practice, for example by undertaking locum sessions, assistantship, retainer schemes.

Self-awareness

It is important to try to listen to yourself consulting. As you do so, check how your performance matches up to the criteria listed under the five domains:

- Data gathering. Are you taking a focused history, doing efficient examinations, making use of information present in the records?
- Doctor patient interaction. Are you listening to the patient, helping them to tell you why they came, eliciting the concerns that underlie their presentation, and checking if you have understood them correctly?
- Communication. Are you communicating well, explaining diagnoses without jargon, in terms that the patient can understand? Are you negotiating treatment rather than issuing doctors' orders?
- Management. Is your management safe, sensible and practical? Are you using resources responsibly? Do you offer options where these are appropriate?
- Anticipatory care. Are you thinking about the future implications for the patient and others, arranging necessary follow-up, providing preventive care and health promotion where needed?

Feedback

Arrange to get feedback from other people. You could ask your patients to comment on your consulting style; you could get your trainer or a colleague to sit in on your surgery and give you feedback; or you could do some simulated consultations with a colleague or in a small group, and help one another.

Review

Ideally, you need to be able to review your own performance. You probably won't be able to use video-recorded live consultations — otherwise you would not be eligible for the simulated surgery. However you may be able to use audio-taping, or you could use video with simulated consultations. Watch your performance with a trusted but objective colleague, and see what you can learn from it.

Timing

This is a potential source of difficulty in the simulated surgery. If you are a very slow consulter, you may not be able to finish within the 10 minutes allowed. If you are a speed merchant, you may be missing out some important elements of the consultation. The solution is to get a stopwatch and time yourself over a number of consultations. You will then know whether action is needed to help you make the best of your allotted 10 minutes.

Language

Do you have a problem with consulting in English? The examiners will make some allowance for those whose first language is not English, but you have to remember that the MRCGP is an examination for competence in British general practice. You will need to understand the problems and concerns of patients who live in the UK, and you will need to speak to them in a way that they can understand. The best thing is to practise with English-speaking patients and to get feedback from people whose first language is English.

Reading

Although practice is essential to mastering the art of consultation, there are some books which will give you useful insight and guidance. A reading list is given in appendix 1 which contains material entirely suitable for the simulated surgery as well as the video method of assessing consulting skills.

Conclusion

The examiners are looking for *Scientia cum Caritas*, both science and consideration. Remember that giving the correct diagnosis and treatment without any concern for the patient is poor medicine, but showing empathy without effectiveness and efficiency is also a disservice to your patient.

See appendix 1 for suggested further reading for this chapter.

7   Paper One: The written paper

Andrew Wilson and Declan Dwyer

Paper 1 is a three-hour paper which is written in free text by candidates and marked individually by examiners, as opposed to the OPSCAN system of machine marking used for Paper 2. Marks are given for content rather than length, and answers given in expanded note form are acceptable. They should be clear and concise.

The paper consists of 12 or more questions to be answered in three hours. Approximately equal time should be spent on each question. Some questions are based on printed material which is presented with the questions, and extra time (typically half an hour) is allowed for candidates to read this material, which usually refers to the critical appraisal section of the paper.

In the examination hall candidates receive a combined question and answer booklet. Each question is printed at the top of a separate page, and answers are written below it on the same sheet. If more room is required, the reverse side of the question sheet may be used. For marking, the question booklet is split up and each page sent to a different examiner. You should therefore answer each question specifically, even if this involves repetition of part of an answer to an earlier question.

How the questions are designed

Three main abilities are tested in the questions, namely:
- Knowledge and interpretation of general practice literature
- Ability to evaluate and interpret written material
- Ability to integrate and apply theoretical knowledge, experience and professional values to solving practical problems encountered within an NHS setting.

Individual questions may focus on one or more of the abilities above. Each key ability will be discussed separately to indicate how they may be approached while preparing for the examination and writing answers on the day.

Questions predominantly designed to test knowledge and interpretation of general practice literature

To pass these you need to be familiar with the current supporting and opposing views on the subject in question. Higher marks will be gained if you can quote sources, and higher still if you can illustrate your familiarity with these sources by a brief critical appraisal or summary of the author's conclusions. Primary (original) papers or books should be mentioned, which should be those known and used by British general practitioners. Major work done abroad is relevant, but little-known work published in foreign journals is not.

Merely memorising and listing references carries very few marks. Recent references are usually more relevant, as is significant work which has stood the test of time. The doctors who mark the paper have access to a databank of world literature about the topic of each question. Inaccurate or incomplete references will not be penalised but misleading ones will be.

When answering these questions the best approach is initially to think and note what you know that is relevant to the answer. You can then follow this up by recalling more about the source of this knowledge, such as the reference, the quality and generalisability of the paper. Starting by try to recall a list of references usually leads to a blank mind! To encourage you in this process the space for answering some questions is laid out with two columns, a left hand one for the evidence (what you know), and the right hand column for you to comment on its source, and the strength and reliability of the evidence. Ensure you fill in the left hand column, even if you can't recall the reference. You may gain enough marks to pass from your knowledge of current evidence without a detailed knowledge of the references.

The question topics usually cover an area of new development or of current interest in general practice, or are based on common clinical problems and their management. Candidates are required to show that they can formulate a modern management plan based on the most recent evidence on the subject.

This evidence usually takes the form of research published in the main journals relevant to general practice, guidelines of national status, RCGP occasional papers, seminal papers on important topics even if written several years ago, systematic reviews, metanalyses and, of course, books. If you cannot remember the precise details of a reference but you know the content, you may, for instance, write 'a leading article in the *BMJ* in 1997', provided you are reasonably sure that this is correct.

The following four examples show the typical topics and wording of this kind of question:

- Discuss the evidence for the use of thrombolytics in the management of acute myocardial infarction.
- Discuss the evidence for the use of antibiotics in acute otitis media
- What are the current views in the management of chronic asthma?
- What is the evidence for the value of cholesterol screening in general practice?

Knowledge of current evidence may be examined by presenting the candidate with clinical situations and asking the candidates for the published evidence which will influence their management plan. An example of this type of question, with discussion of how to approach a suitable answer, is given in example question 7.1 on page 106.

Questions which test ability to evaluate and interpret written material

You will usually be presented with short pieces of written material in the form of extracts from a published paper, a summary of a research paper, the methods or results sections of a paper on their own, or an editorial or other extract from a leading journal. You will be asked to critically appraise this presented material. This will test your ability to:

- Recognize the main types of study design and the strengths and weaknesses of each
- Identify the sources of bias and the efforts made to eliminate it
- Evaluate the validity and reliability of these studies

You will be expected to interpret any results of presented material, which requires a knowledge of confidence intervals, numbers needed to treat (NNT), odds ratios, sensitivity, specificity and predictive values. You may be asked to apply the results of the paper to a clinical scenario.

Questions which test ability to integrate and apply theoretical knowledge and professional values to practical problems encountered within an NHS setting

These questions are about everyday life and practice, including how to solve a variety of problems. Their strength lies in asking questions that are in context to the general practitioner's work. Candidates often ask, 'What is the syllabus?' This is rather like asking, 'How long is a piece of string?' or, 'What challenges will I meet in the surgery tomorrow?'. By nature general practice is full of uncertainty and the unexpected, and that is part of its charm and excitement.

The questions you may expect in the MRCGP are grounded in real general practice where common things are common, and the skills learned in solving one problem can be used equally well with a new, unexpected problem. A typical paper will include questions on individual patient care, the practice team and its management and wider political, social and ethical issues. A guide to some of the broad areas from which topics are selected is given in figure 7.1 (page 100).

There seem to be two major processes appropriate to solving problems. Some are amenable to a logical deductive approach using systematic thinking. An example of a question requiring this kind of approach is:

Shirley Owen, a 45-year-old housewife, attends for the injection of her tennis elbow (lateral epicondylitis). Give a step-by-step account of how you would proceed.

Figure 7.1   *Areas of competence from which questions are selected for Paper 1*

- Skills in problem solving, prioritising and decision making in a wide range of clinical settings

- Insight into the psychological processes affecting the patient, the doctor, and the relationship between them

- Recognition of the family, social, occupational, environmental and cultural contexts of ill health

- Communication and consultation skills

- Understanding the principles of preventive medicine and the promotion of good health

- Attitude to patients, colleagues and staff

- Appropriate use of resources, including drugs, treatment facilities, referral agencies, other members of the health care team, ancillary staff and complementary practitioners

- Appreciation of ethical principles and the general practitioner's terms of service

- Awareness of current or foreseeable trends and developments in primary care

---

Others require a more lateral-thinking approach. An example of this kind is:

What may be the effects of advances in information technology on the care of patients?

Candidates may have thought about and discussed the latter problem, as it is topical. Even if they had not, they should have developed skills for solving other problems in the past which could be applied to this situation.

When marking the papers the examiners look for performance across the main themes, or constructs, appropriate to the question. These are important content areas of the answer describing single themes which are independent of each other. Let us take an example:

Jane, aged 5, has recurrent secretory otitis media. Outline how you would choose between the management options.

One theme that could be followed might be clinical information, including aspects of history taking, examination and investigations. Others might include resources and their availability, the child and parents' views and the clinical evidence on the effectiveness of interventions. These are separate themes, and a candidate could do well or badly in each, quite independently, and would receive marks appropriate to performance in each one. Note that this question includes the abilities of both problem solving and knowledge of current literature.

In writing your answers, include what you think or would try in real life. Do try and show the examiner that you are caring and competent doctor. Do not guess the constructs as this is neither necessary nor helpful. They are a tool to aid marking, and the examiner will find the marks for you if you have given the information. For instance, in a question about a consultation they would ask themselves, 'If I were an informed patient, how would I judge the quality of the consultation this answer describes', and judge the answer in the light of the constructs they have already identified. A good consultation is appropriate to the patient's needs; for instance, empathy may be appropriate with the recently widowed, but not such a high priority with the businessman who wants his hepatitis injection before travelling abroad.

The aim in these answers should be to show the examiner that you really understand the issues. We don't mind how you do it, but be sure to write clearly and concisely. This may be difficult under exam conditions, though you can often ensure that the examiner knows what you are thinking by giving examples of what you mean. There are no rules about style of presentation, just communicate your message to the examiner. Short notes, prose, diagrams — even poetry — are all acceptable. You may choose to order your answer under headings, or to write an essay. All are acceptable, and the examiner will look for marks wherever they can be found. Do your best with handwriting. The examiners will work hard to read anything you write, but they can't give you marks for the totally illegible!

Some candidates find it helpful to use aides memoires to ensure they think of everything, such as:

- 'Physical, psychological and social'
- 'Immediate, short term and long term'
- 'The patient, the doctor, the practice and society'

By all means use these if they are relevant and helpful, but avoid them if they are not appropriate to the question. Many candidates fail to do themselves justice by trying to force an answer into an inappropriate framework, thereby emphasising irrelevant issues, and leaving out important ones. Some features that characterise a good answer are shown in figure 7.2.

Figure 7.2   *Characteristics of a good answer to problem solving questions*

The good candidate:

- Reads each question carefully, and answers it as asked
- Thinks in a wide ranging way, but realistically, about how a competent and sensitive general practitioner would deal with each scenario
- Avoids jargon, cliches and over generalisation
- Includes illustrative details, explanations and relevant examples

---

Preparation for Paper 1

Paper 1 tests a wide variety of areas and therefore preparing for it should begin early, if possible during hospital training but, at the latest, at the start of the practice year. The advice on preparation given below is discussed under three headings:

- Knowledge of the literature
- Critical appraisal
- Problem solving

Knowledge of the literature

This needs to be broad based and related to problems encountered in general practice. It is recommended that you keep a notebook at your clinical desk and list problems encountered during training or preparation for the exam. Each week you should search the medical database on these problems and note the evidence and strength of evidence related to them. Two hours a week spent in this activity will ensure that you cover the areas in which questions are most likely to be asked, both in this paper and, indeed, other parts of the examination.

Concurrently, you should be reading journals, such as the *British Journal of General Practice, the British Medical Journal, The Practitioner, Update, Bandolier* and *Evidence Based Medicine,* to see what issues are in the news. Work through the preceding two years' issues. Read the title of every article and, where it is relevant to general practice, the summary. You soon notice that some topics are appearing frequently. These could be 'hot' topics likely to be picked by the examiners when selecting topics for questions. Gather articles together under topic headings, follow references and read more deeply. Particularly important are editorials, review articles and metanalyses, and RCGP occasional papers. These will refer you to important papers in other journals, and in such a way an overview of the literature will be built up. Topical issues are important, so keep an eye on the news section of the *British Medical Journal,* and the national newspapers.

A group working together is always better at this sort of task than the individual alone, and you should try to join a journal club early in your training. You will soon find that a group can share out the job of ploughing through the literature. Remember the importance, and the educational value, of books. Because several papers that still influence clinical management were written some time ago, however, it is important to study the literature by pursuing specific topics rather than covering recent journals issue by issue. Six valuable pieces of advice are given in figure 7.3.

Figure 7.3   *Six pieces of advice for reading the literature*

1 Relate your reading to problems encountered in general practice

2 Research topics rather than reading consecutive back issues of journals

3 Team up with a group of doctors preparing for the examination

4 Obtain help from your postgraduate centre librarian to find influential books and computerised search facilities

5 Concentrate on articles that have most influenced current practice rather than the most recent published papers

6 It is more important to know what a paper is about than who wrote it or where it was published

---

It is a good idea to use your exam preparation group to brainstorm likely topics. Questions are often based on subjects that are of interest because they are common and involve many patients. Sometimes there has been a recent change in practice because of a major research paper, which will attract the examiners' attention. Good examples of this are the ISIS trials of the treatment of myocardial infarction and the recommendations of the British Thoracic Society on asthma. Both publications have prompted examination questions in the past, and could well have been anticipated by astute candidates during preparation.

Critical appraisal

Critical appraisal is about deciding on the merits of the material presented to you by balancing its strengths against its flaws and deciding whether the conclusions are likely to be valid and whether they are clinically important. Applied common sense is a good description of this process. The same common sense is valuable in interpreting and applying research results.

However, it is helpful early in your training to become familiar with some structure or model for appraising research papers. Much has been written on the subject, and particularly recommended is the series of articles in the *Journal of the American Medical Association* during 1993-95. Entitled *Users' Guides to the Medical Literature*, they cover the entire area of critical appraisal. Articles have also been written in the *British Medical Journal*.

When you are reading a paper to assimilate knowledge you may find the discussion section of a paper the most interesting. Critical appraisal, however, concentrates entirely on the methods and results sections. You should develop a method to enable you to determine whether the results obtained are likely to be valid (that is: was the methodology satisfactory?), and to work out what the results are and whether they will help you in caring for your patients. You should practise critical appraisal as often as possible so that it becomes second nature when reading a research paper.

At first it is best done in groups, but later you will find it becomes an automatic process so that it barely holds you up while reading a paper, and you can rapidly reach an opinion as to its strengths and weaknesses. A working knowledge of statistics is important, but statistics form only a small part of critical appraisal. It is often not realised how little candidates need to know. A short guide to the range of statistical knowledge expected for the MRCGP exam is given in appendix 2.

Problem solving questions

Any challenge may appear among these questions — just as in day-to-day general practice. The more experience you gain in thinking through and solving problems at work the more your problem-solving skills will develop, and the better you will become as both a doctor and a candidate.The best preparation for this part of the exam is experience combined with reflection. The best candidates have a sequential structure to their learning in which they:

- See patients
- Reflect on what they see
- Discuss issues with colleagues and trainers
- Relate them to their reading of the book and journal literature of general practice
- Apply the lessons to future challenges.

The best additional preparation is to work through old papers with a group of peers. It is intended that in future these will be available on the College's web site (http:/www.rcgp.org.uk). As an individual you will probably think of only parts of an answer. Comparing your answers as a group you will come up with all the answers the examiners produce . You can then get an idea of your weaker areas and develop your thinking accordingly. To learn about practice management and teamwork, get involved with it in your own practice. Look critically at how things are done. Learn from the successful, and look critically at the less successful.

Examiners, like candidates, are working doctors, so the same sort of issues will be on their minds as on yours. Always remember that the examiners are marking the paper from the standpoint of patient care. The question they ask is: 'If I were the patient, what would I think of the quality of care indicated in that candidate's answer?'

Examples of questions

Some of these examples are based on relevant references from the literature, others on less specific issues. Each is followed by a commentary which indicates the range of knowledge and understanding which a good answer would demonstrate.

Example question 7.1

Discuss any published evidence which might influence you to attempt blood pressure reduction in the three patients whose average blood pressures after serial measurements are shown:

1 A man of 58 years. He recently suffered a transient ischaemic attack. Blood pressure 150/95

2 A man of 40 years. His 45-year-old brother has angina. His father died of a myocardial infarction aged 50 years. Blood pressure 145/92.

3 A woman of 70 years with no cardiovascular risk factors or adverse clinical findings. Blood pressure 175/95.

Commentary example 7.1

The question looks for evidence in favour of treating mild hypertension. The scenarios involve:

a) A person with target organ damage
b) A person with a strong cardiovascular risk factor
c) An elderly patient

The knowledge required to answer this question well is contained in a variety of references which are numbered in brackets in the following paragraphs and listed in figure 7.4 (see page 109). This degree of detail is not expected in an answer, but is given here to start the reader on a literature search.

The British Hypertension Society (1) would recommend treatment in all three cases. All would probably benefit from non-pharmacological treatment (1, 2). In individual cases the following are relevant:

Case 1

There is a 42% reduction in stroke; average diastolic blood pressure reduction of 5-6 mm Hg and only 2-3 years treatment (3). This matches results from long term prospective observational studies of the effects of different levels of blood pressure suggesting that the benefits appear rapidly (4). This patient is a high risk individual with possibly a 5-10% risk of stroke per year. In this situation the absolute reduction in stroke risk might be substantial. Published trials used mainly diuretics.

Case 2

The benefits of treating blood pressure to prevent coronary heart disease are less clear, but the evidence points to significant benefit.

107

An overview of trials shows a 14% reduction in CHD (3). Because CHD is more common than stroke, the absolute number who might benefit could be considerable. Observational studies (4) would suggest that twice this number ought to benefit. This would suggest that some other chronic process (eg atherosclerosis) may be mediating the effects of blood pressure on CHD. Alternatively the drugs could have toxic effects on the heart.

Case 3

The evidence suggests a reduction of both stroke and CHD (5,6,7). One trial suggested that low dose diuretic treatment was superior to beta-blockers.

Good answers to this question require a knowledge of major trials, and demonstration of such knowledge would be reflected in the marks awarded. Figure 7.4 (see page 109) lists some papers that would be relevant in this example.

Example question 7.2

Evaluate shared care in diabetes between hospital consultants and general practitioners

Commentary on example 7.2

A good answer would have to cover the following areas:

• Many earlier schemes involved shifted rather than shared care

• Trials of structured care show favourable results in comparison with unstructured care

• There is concern that the increase in shared care since 1990 may be mainly financially led. The previous trials were in enthusiastic practices

• There has to be a greater than normal information exchange eg shared record cards, liaison meetings

> *Figure 7.4   Reference on which a good answer to example question 7.1 would be based*
>
> 1 Ramsay L, Williams B, Dennis Johnstone G, et al. British Hypertension Society guidelines for hypertension management 1999: summary (1999) *British Medical Journal* 319, 630-635.
>
> 2 Treatment of Mild Hypertension Research Group (1991) The treatment of mild hypertension study — a randomised placebo controlled trial of nutritional hygienic regimen along with various drug mono-therapies. *Archives of Internal Medicine* 151, 1413-23.
>
> 3 Collins R, Peto R and MacMahon S et al.(1990) Blood pressure, stroke and coronary heart disease, Part 2. Short-term reductions in blood pressure: overview of randomised drug trials in their epidemiological context. *The Lancet* 335, 827-38.
>
> 4 MacMahon S, Peto R and Cutler J et al. (1990) Blood pressure, stroke and coronary heart disease, Part 1. Prolonged differences in blood pressure: prospective observational studies corrected for the regression dilution bias. *The Lancet* 335, 765-764.
>
> 5 Amery A, Birkenhager W and Brixko P et al. (1985) Mortality and morbidity results from the European Working Party on high blood pressure in the elderly trial. *The Lancet* 1 (1985), 1349-1354.
>
> 6 SHEP Co-operative Research Group (1991) Prevention of stroke by anti-hypertensive drug treatment in older persons with isolated systolic hypertension. *Journal of the American Medical Association* 265, 3255-64.
>
> 7 Medical Research Council Working Party (1992) MRC trial of treatment of hypertension in older adults, principal results. *British Medical Journal* 304, 405-12.

- Schemes are either centralised, hospital based and consultant led or decentralised,community based and multidisciplinary

- The role of the hospital varies, eg periodic reviews, initial review and stabilisation, insulin treated patients, retinal screening

- In the community there may be mini-clinics, nurse co-ordinated care, 'diabetes-days' etc. Opticians can screen eyes. Chiropodists and dieticians may be present

- Factors which contribute to successful schemes include well defined objectives, written guidelines, enthusiastic participants, diabetic nurses, patient registers for recall and review, patients actively involved in their own management, teamwork, diabetic resource centres.

All these points were contained in *Occasional Paper 67, Shared Care for Diabetes*, a systematic review; Greenhalgh PM, RCGP 1994. Candidates who indicated this would gain marks. Anyone quoting any of the schemes reviewed would be very impressive.

The outline given above would represent the basis of a perfect answer, but the short time available in the examination makes it unlikely that anyone would produce all of it. An understanding of the factors that make shared care schemes successful is particularly important and candidates who covered this well would be marked higher than those who did not. Figure 7.5 (see page 111) gives some indication of the different standards of answer that might be given and how they would be marked.

Example question 7.3

Candidates are presented with the summary only of the following paper:

> Evaluation of the diagnostic value of pneumatic otoscopy in primary care using the results of tympanometry as a reference standard. De Melker R (1993) *British Journal of General Practice* 43, 22.

Figure 7.5   Example question 7.2: the range of answers and how they would be marked

High mark
Candidates would have a wide knowledge touching at least in brief on most aspects of the model answer. Others would cover fewer points but would review them in depth introducing evidence from papers.

Average mark
About half the points would be identified including some discussion of factors which make shared care successful. Some relevant literature would be quoted but its use would usually be superficial.

Low mark
At most only three points from the answer would be covered and then only briefly. Clinical rather than organisational aspects of diabetic care might be included. Any references would be irrelevant.

What would encourage you to read the rest of the presented article and what would discourage you?

(The complete text of the material presented is given in appendix 2)

Commentary on example 7.3

The wording of this question clearly invites two major headings, namely factors that encourage and those that discourage. A good answer would list these factors and expand them in brief discussion. The following answer is long but not unattainable by a good candidate.

A model answer to example 7.3

A) *Factors that encourage*

Presentation: Clear aim, well-described methods — it appears to be an appropriate evaluation of a screening test.

Relevance: Glue ear is a common, important general practice problem. It is potentially treatable, but controversy and difficulty surround the best route to diagnosis.

Intervention: Need to read on to know more about the potential place of pneumatic otoscopy in primary care, about the rationale for the study, and about arguments for asking the question in the first place: why is it better than ordinary otoscopy or a whisper test? What are its advantages compared with going for the gold standard directly?

Generalisability and consequences:

• Uncertain whether the patient population and results are generalisable, so need to read to decide

• How does the prevalence in a sample like this compare with the prevalence in a typical primary care population?

• Process described is potentially generalisable to practice (trained nurse using equipment in surgery), but need more on consequences: Could the GP do it? If a specially trained nurse is needed: what training, workload, quality control? Costs of equipment and maintenance? Costs and benefits against alternatives in primary care? What effect on referral rates — does it simply add a layer of time and trouble without altering the outcome for the patient?

Selection: The patient selection might be a discouragement but if not, need details of results to help judge generalisation and consequences: how many cases were actually missed because of low sensitivity?

B) *Factors that discourage*

Presentation and relevance: The results as presented in the abstract are rambling and contain jargon. No figures are given for the important results, so a clear message does not come through. Most of the results presented in the abstract seem irrelevant to the main purpose and confuse rather than enlighten (for example young children more likely than old to have abnormal otoscopy).

Intervention: What is pneumatic otoscopy? Why is it important? Since there is not immediate and simple statement about why this might change practice to advantage, then this is a discouragement.

Generalisability and selection: Nature and selection of subjects is unclear, but the suggestion is that they were not a typical sample of patients as seen in routine primary care. The age range is wide compared with the critical age range for glue ear problems in primary care.

Example question 7.4

Candidates are presented with the summary, methods and results sections, and the tables from the following paper:

Breast Cancer: causes of patients' distress identified by qualitative analysis. *British Journal of General Practice* (1994) 44, 370-371.

How far does the information given under methods, results and tables support the authors' conclusions as stated in the summary?

(The complete text of the material presented is given in appendix 3)

Commentary on example 7.4

The important points which a good answer would contain are set out in the model below. Notice how the response is given in expanded note form with abbreviations and enumerations.

Model answer to example 7.4

Conclusions in the paper are:

1 Patients suffer distress in areas of management that doctors do not suspect important

2 Qualitative analysis can identify these areas.

Information in the methods section

1 Technique seems likely to pick up distressing experiences. Qualitative research is difficult and alien to doctors!

2 Single interviewer likely to be consistent

3 Interviews conducted over a three-year period and in only two practices — reduces validity

4 Interviews cover events retrospectively and some events, eg first diagnosis, were clearly further back in time than others, eg prosthesis problems. May affect recall

5 Experience rather than strength of distress was recalled. Important cf doctor's questionnaire

6 Use of trigger words may vary with patient's personality type, introducing bias

7 Doctors circulated with their questionnaire at end of study. May reduce validity

8 Doctors asked about all breast cancer patients, not just those in the study

9 Doctors asked to rank order events in terms of perceived frequency — this is simply not comparable with what the patients were asked to do.

Information in results section

1 Only 26 ex 39 eligible women interviewed. High drop-out rate ?Current disease status

2 Very small sample, particularly for a disease that has such a wide range of natural history

3 Variety of treatment regimes — ?Similar to that seen by the doctors questioned

4 Very poor response from doctors. ?Validity. ?Attempt to improve reply rate

5 Value of anecdotal comment. (In view of frequency of ca breast it is highly likely that several doctors had affected relatives).

Information from tables

1 Of the eight categories that doctors were asked to rank, the spread of numbers was only 11-15. Highly unlikely to be statistically significant. No statistics applied

2 Category about problems with doctors also had 11 votes but was omitted from the rank order list. Why?

Comments in conclusion

1 Authors conclusions are not justified because the methodology of the study precludes that question being answered. Would need to ask the doctors what areas they thought caused patients' distress

2 Qualitative analysis may be able to pick out areas of distress, but the technique is not put to good use here.

Except for the few candidates taking the simulated surgery in place the videotaped consultations in the consulting skills module there is no opportunity to observe clinical examination in the MRCGP. It is therefore occasionally asked about in Paper 1, and the following is typical of such a question.

Example question 7.5

Kevin O'Connell, a 38-year-old roofer, has a painful knee. Describe your examination and how it might influence your diagnosis and management.

Commentary on example 7.5

In answering this question the good candidate will:

• Describe how to examine the knee in a structured, and sensitive way, explaining what they are looking for and including an assessment of function

• Address any issues of general examination of the patient both physical and psychological

• Relate the examination to possible diagnoses, taking the given history into account

• Show an understanding of the management options, related to the history and examination

• Show awareness of social issues, such as the patient's occupation, and the patient's wishes.

Example question 7.6

Mrs Betty Coombs is 80 years old and lives alone. Her son writes to inform you that her memory is terrible and she recently had a small kitchen fire. How might you help?

Commentary on example 7.6

A good candidate will:

• Show a wide range of options for broad based information gathering, such as more information from her son, other primary health care team members, and social services. A home visit and psychogeriatric assessment may be considered. Issues of physical illness such as cerebro-vascular accident, hypothyroidism, and Alzheimer's might be considered. Psychological problems such as depression, and drug taking such as alcohol and medication may be relevant.

• Address the issue of risk assessment. This will depend both on her own abilities, and hazards in the house such as cookers, gas fires, the house opening onto a main road. Others, such as an occupational therapist may be able to help.

• Make appropriate use of available support in the community. This might include family, home carers, meals on wheels, the health visitor and nurses, the community psychiatric nurse, voluntary agencies, the availability of sheltered housing and appropriate follow up.

• Show awareness of legal, ethical and family issues. Balancing the patient's wish for autonomy with the risk to herself and others. Consider the son's concerns, expectations and motives, and legal issues.

Example question 7.7

Your new general practitioner partner registers with your practice. When his notes arrive you discover he has a long history of severe depressive illness. What implications does this have?

Commentary on example 7.7

Read the question carefully! The word implications means just that. It does not just mean consequences, but includes implications about issues before as well as after the event. A good candidate will:

• Address issues of selection and interview. Should this have been picked up at that stage? Was the application form honestly filled in? What about the references?

• Consider the practical problems. If there are further problems, how to cover the work, costs, ability to cope with certain types of patients, recognizing further problems, the dangers of self-management and the practice agreement.

• Recognize the emotional issues. There may be anger and insecurity in the new and existing partners.

• See the potential for conflict. This might occur within the team or between the new partner and patients. Taking sides may occur within the practice and there may be conflicts of interest such as how to balance looking after the care of patients with looking after the needs of the new partner and others in the team.

• Recognize issues of confidentiality. Who in the team should know? What to tell patients during periods of depression?

Example question 7.8

How may your experience of consulting with patients be used to further your education and development?

Commentary on example 7.8

A good candidate will:

• Recognize that doctors learn from patients. Patients may bring information from newspapers and increasingly the Internet. They may report investigations and treatments carried out by specialists. Good ideas for management may be originated by the patients themselves, and feedback on performance gained from patients and their families.

• Understand that consultation skills and awareness of the doctor-patient relationship may be enhanced by reflecting on what goes on in real consultations, perhaps with the help of Balint groups and videotaping, integrating this with reading on the consultation.

• See that audit may help to look at performance, relate it to external standards and those of peers, and plan new approaches and strategies. Critical incident analysis may show opportunities to learn from failures.

• Recognize that reflecting on experiences will help to identify learning needs, and address these by thought, discussion and reading.

• Know that this is the best way to prepare for Paper 1!

The last four examples are not perfect answers, but include the sort of areas that a very good candidate would cover. A distinction candidate would cover most of the areas well, with clear explanations and examples. A satisfactory candidate would cover many of the areas, and though missing out several would give an adequate description or examples to show that he or she understood the issues. A poor candidate would leave out many of the areas, and in those that were covered it would be unclear whether they were really understood.

The candidates who do best in Paper 1 are those who look for as much experience in practice as possible, and then are curious, thoughtful and reflective about what they see, integrating their experience with reading, thought and discussion about the problems they have encountered. It is a paper set in the context of everyday practice.

8   Paper Two: 'The MCQ'

David Sales

Paper 2 is the machine-marked written module of the MRCGP, still affectionately known to many as the MCQ, which is designed to test both your knowledge about general practice and, more importantly, the deeper understanding and application of that knowledge. Every question in this module is intended to explore a topic in which an ordinary GP or registrar could be expected to have a working knowledge. Three hours is allowed to answer Paper 2, which is offered in May and October, on the same day as Paper 1.

Rationale

In an ideal world of unlimited resources most educators and examinees would prefer free response or prose questions in examinations. Such questions can test important reasoning skills and they have high validity because the examinee has to construct an answer rather than simply recognising it in a list. However, prose questions have a number of significant disadvantages, notably:

- Indeterminacy regarding the focus and purpose of questions, the depth and specificity of detail desired in the response
- Cumbersome, time consuming and resource intensive hand scoring with the potential for subjectivity
- Content coverage, with few items being tested per unit time and the risk of contamination or leakage of questions

Much of general practice involves the management of uncertainty, and understandably general practitioners often feel reluctant to commit themselves. With patients' illnesses we are generally dealing with shades of grey rather than the black and white certainties invited by traditional multiple true-false questions. However, it is axiomatic that possession of factual knowledge is essential for competent general practice and this contributes to the delivery of gold standard patient care. Paper 2 affords the ideal method of assessing this knowledge and has several significant advantages over prose questions, notably the ability to test the breadth of knowledge in the time available, and the ease and objectivity of scoring. The following account describes the questions in terms of their construction, content and format.

Construction of the questions

The Paper 2 development group currently comprises eight examiners who are all general practitioner principals with an interest in postgraduate education, and an educationalist who advises on statistical issues. Proposed questions, each of which must be referenced, are submitted to the panel for rigorous peer scrutiny prior to inclusion in the paper.

Great care is taken to ensure that Paper 2 is as fair as possible, and questions are carefully selected according to the following criteria:

- Validity: the question must accurately test what we wish it to test and what we think it tests.
- Relevance: the questions should be totally relevant to general practice; any topic covered can be one which occurs commonly, or one which is deemed significant but less common.
- Degree of difficulty: the discriminatory power of a question will be poor if the question is so difficult that no candidate can answer it or so easy that all candidates answer it correctly.
- Clarity: there should be no possible misinterpretation of the combined stem and item which forms the question.

Clarity is vital for fairness, so in an attempt to reduce ambiguity we have tried to define precisely the conventional terms that are used in Paper 2. An analogy is the way in which for years weather forecasters talked of isolated, scattered or occasional showers. But what was the difference between them? The public certainly didn't know, so now the forecast predicts a 10% chance of a shower (isolated), 30% (scattered) and 50% (occasional). Similarly, every effort is made to ensure that the wording of questions is clear and unambiguous as possible.

For the purposes of the examination certain conventional terms have the following meanings:

- 'Pathognomic', 'diagnostic', 'characteristic' and 'in the vast majority' imply that a feature would occur in at least 60% of cases
- 'In the majority' implies that a feature occurs in greater than 50% of cases
- 'In the minority' implies that a feature occurs in less than 50% of cases
- 'Low chance' and 'in a substantial minority' imply that a feature may occur in up to 30% of cases
- 'Has been shown', 'recognised' and 'reported' all refer to evidence which can be found in an authoritative medical text. None of these terms makes any implication about the frequency with which the feature occurs.

These terms are reproduced in the introduction of your exam paper, so you don't have to memorise them!

Content of the questions

In terms of content, the paper comprises questions of relevance to general practice from the following key areas.

- Core knowledge
- Emerging knowledge, defined as having been published in the 18 months prior to each exam
- Application of knowledge
- Critical appraisal including knowledge of statistics, research and methodology sufficient to evaluate published papers

The number of items in each of these areas is constantly under review and inevitably there is some overlap between them. Currently, around 10-15% of the paper consists of critical appraisal questions, which test your ability to interpret data. You will need to have a basic understanding of the commonly used statistical terms, including those used in evidence-based medicine, eg calculation of number needed to treat (NNT). Calculators are not necessary for such questions and so are not allowed in the exam. Some of these questions relate to current best practice and they should be answered in relation to generally available published evidence rather than based on your local arrangements.

Questions are constructed using a blueprint with a finite number of themes, eg abdominal pain, as shown in table 8.1. The purpose of this is to ensure that as many areas as possible are sampled, and duplication is avoided. Thus in the example given in table 8.1, if questions on abdominal pain were asked they would variously sample knowledge of it in patients of different ages, and competence in diagnosis, management and critical appraisal, rather than, say, three questions on investigation.

Table 8.1: Example of a Paper 2 blueprint

Theme	Diagnosis	Investigation (selection/ interpretation of diagnostic tests)	Management	Critical Appraisal (analysis and interpretation data including audit)
Abdominal pain: Acute				
Childhood				
Adulthood				
Elderly				
Abdominal pain: chronic				
Childhood				
Adulthood				
Elderly				

The questions appear in random order on the paper, that is to say not all the questions in each subject area are grouped together or appear in the order listed above.

Format of the questions

In respect of question format, the paper is in two distinct sections.

The first section

This contains questions in the following formats, examples of which are given as examples 8.1 to 8.4:

• Single best answer (SBA) questions in which a statement or stem is followed by a variable number of items, only one of which is correct
• Multiple best answer (MBA) questions in which a statement is followed by a variable number of items, a specified number of which are correct
• Extending matching questions (EMQ) in which a scenario has to be matched to an answer from a list of options. You may feel that there are several possible answers but you must choose only the most likely from the option list
• Summary completion questions which test your critical reading ability from a summary of a paper presented in the question paper

At the time of writing there is a maximum of 120 items in this section. As a rule of thumb, about one minute per item should be allowed for section 1, that is two of the three hours available for the paper.

Example 8.1   A single best answer question

In the management of croup in a two-year old child, which single best treatment has been shown in randomised controlled clinical trials to shorten the course of the condition?

A   Place the child in a steam-filled bathroom

B   Administer inhaled budesonide

C   Prescribe amoxycillin 125 mg t.d.s. for 5 days

D   Administer inhaled salbutamol

E   Prescribe paediatric cough suppressant containing codeine

F   Administer inhaled tribavirin

Correct answer: B

Reference: *BMJ* 1995, 311, 1244

Example 8.2   A multiple best answer (MBA) question

A 65-year-old male smoker presents with a gradual onset of
breathlessness on moderate exertion, and a cough with clear
sputum. Chest examination reveals general reduction of breath
sounds and the presence of a few rhonchi bilaterally.
Spirometry reveals an FEV1 of 50% of predicted. Identify the
three most appropriate therapeutic interventions to be
considered following the British Thoracic Society COPD
guidelines 1997. Give three answers.

A   Salbutamol inhaler

B   Beclomethasone inhaler

C   Ipratropium inhaler

D   Salmeterol inhaler

E   Sodium cromoglycate inhaler

F   Oral theophylline

G   Oral steroid trial

H   Nebulised ipratropium

I   Referral for long term oxygen therapy

Correct answers: A,   C,   G

Example 8.3   An extended matching question

Theme: chest pain
Options:

A	Angina pectoris	H	Mitral stenosis
B	Aortic stenosis	I	Musculoskeletal pain
C	Compression fracture spine	J	Myocardial infarction
D	Dissecting aneurysm	K	Pericarditis
E	Herpes zoster	L	Pneumonia
F	Hyperventilation	M	Pneumothorax
G	Oesophageal spasms	N	Pulmonary embolism

Instructions:

For each patient below select the most likely diagnosis. Each option may be used once, more than once or not at all.

Items:

1   A 55-year-old business man who ruptured his right Achilles tendon one month previously and has his leg in a plaster of Paris

cylinder. He complains of progressive shortness of breath and chest pain worse on taking a deep breath.

2   A 20-year-old shop assistant who complains that she cannot get her breath, that her chest feels tight and her fingers are numb. Her peak flow is normal and her chest is clear. You note that she is breathing rapidly.

3   A 78-year-old man who following a head cold became short of breath and developed a cough productive of yellow sputum. He is pyrexial and you note areas of diminished breath sounds with fine crepitations at the right base.

4   A 55-year-old man presents with sudden onset of crushing central chest pain at 4.00 am. He is vomiting and sweating, very frightened and his blood pressure is 100/55.

5   An 80-year-old woman lives in sheltered accommodation. She has had falls with loss of consciousness from which she makes a quick recovery. She admits to chest pain on exertion and to feeling giddy. She has a basal systolic murmur radiating to the neck.

6   A 19-year-old student has sudden onset of severe pain in the left side of his chest. He is very short of breath and is slightly cyanosed. His left lung is resonant with absent breath sounds.

Correct answers: 1 N,   2 F,   3 L,   4 J,   5 B,   6 M

Example 8.4   A summary completion question

An extract from a published paper is presented. Its subject is :

The effects of obesity and weight-loss on left ventricular mass and relative wall thickness: survey and intervention study. (British Medical Journal 1997, 315, 912-6)

First read the following extract from the subjects and methods section of the paper.

In total, 119 subjects from the city of Gothenburg and the surrounding areas were enrolled, comprising 61 men and 58 women with ages ranging from 37 to 61 years. The study population consisted of two groups of obese patients (body mass index 30-47 kg/m2) and one group of non-obese subjects (body mass index 18-27 kg/m2). The obese subjects were recruited from the ongoing Swedish obese subjects study, which is a nationwide trial designed to determine whether the mortality and morbidity among obese people who lose weight by surgical means differs from that in an obese reference group. The non-obese subjects were recruited from a randomly selected sample of adults living in the muncipality of Mölndal.

The two groups of obese subjects comprised 41 consecutive patients referred for weight reducing gastric surgery (the obese operation group) and 35 matched control subjects who were treated with conventional dietary recommendations (obese control group). The non-obese group consisted of 43 subjects matched with the obese groups for sex, age and height. Subjects in all three study groups were examined at baseline and those in the two obese groups were examined again after one year. Four of the obese control patients were excluded from the study as they did not participate in the follow up, leaving 31 subjects in the obese control group.

Body weight was measured with the subjects wearing light clothing and no shoes and was rounded to the nearest 0.1 kg. Height measurements were rounded to the nearest 0.01 m, and body mass index was calculated as the weight in kilograms divided by height in metres squared.

Systolic and diastolic (phase V) blood pressure was measured in the right arm using a mercury sphygmomanometer with the subject in the supine position after 10 minutes of rest. An appropriate cuff was used, with a width of at least 40% of the circumference of the arm. Echocardiography was performed on each subject in the left lateral decubitus position, using a commercially available ultrasound system

(Accuson 128 XP: Mountain View, CA) with 2.0 - 2.5 MHZ transducers. Two dimensional echocardiography registrations were obtained with short axis and four chamber views. From the left ventricular short axis view, epicardial and endocardial perimeters were traced and mean wall thickness and cavity radius were calculated. Relative wall thickness was defined as the ratio of mean wall thickness to chamber radius. Left ventricular mass was calculated according to the truncated ellipsoid algorithm from Byrd et al. Left ventricular diastolic volumes were estimated from the four chamber view, using the disc summation method (modified Simpson's rule).

All recordings were performed by doctors experienced in echo-cardiography, and 75% of the registrations were made by one investigator (IW). Each reading was assessed before statistical analyses took place, and only subjects with recordings of excellent or good quality were included in data analyses. As a result, 9 (13%) of the obese patients were excluded from the analyses of left ventricular wall thickness and mass and 20 (28%) from the estimations of left ventricular volumes. Only 1 (2%) of the lean subjects was excluded from data analyses because of deficient registrations. The standard error of a single determination of left ventricular mass among obese subjects was 17%, assessed by a double determination in nine patients.

Now look at this critique, which outlines the limitations of the design and method of the study. For each of the numbered gaps in the critique choose one word from the following list which best completes the sense, and mark the corresponding lozenge on your answer sheet.

Although the authors attempted to carefully match the subjects in each group for clinical (1)........, this was neither a (2)........ nor a (3)........ study. Evaluation of obese subjects echocardiographically was (4)........ ; this resulted in (5)........ of patients and missing data which could have led to (6)........ in the results. Only one blood pressure recording was taken; this may be (7)........ of blood pressure over time and the lack of (8)........ in measuring blood pressure in obese patients must cast doubt on the (9)........ of the results. This could explain the relatively weak (10)........ of changes in blood pressure and changes in left ventricular structure observed in the study. Other studies have demonstrated the (11) . . . . between blood pressure monitoring and left ventricular mass.

A association	H exclusion	O sensitivity
B bias	I precision	P success
C blinded	J correlation	Q typical
D cohort	K randomised	R undertaken
E demonstrated	L reliability	S unrepresentative
F difficult	M safety	T validity
G error	N selection	U variables

Correct answers to example 8.4

1	U	variables	7	S	unrepresentative
2	K	randomised	8	I	precision
3	C	blinded	9	L	reliability
4	F	difficult	10	A	association
5	H	exclusion	11	J	correlation
6	B	bias			

The second section

This contains the standard multiple true false questions which comprise a statement followed by a variable number of items any, all, or none of which may be correct. At the time of writing there is a maximum of 180 items in this section. The format is familiar to many, but for the sake of completeness an example is given.

Example 8.5   A multiple true/false question

In acne:

1. Topical antibiotics have been shown to be superior to topical benzoyl peroxide.

2. Pseudomembraneous colitis is a recognised complication of treatment with topical clindamycin.

3. Typically there are no further benefits from continuing oral antibiotic therapy beyond six months.

4. Minocycline has been shown to be more effective than oxytetracycline.

5. Tetracycline has been shown to possess a direct anti-inflammatory action.

6. Dairy products are recognised to reduce the absorption of doxycycline.

Correct answers:	1 false	2 true	3 true
	4 false	5 true	6 false

Marking

The scoring of all question formats is the same: candidates are awarded one mark for each item answered correctly. Marks are not deducted for incorrect answers or for failure to answer; the total score on the paper is the number of correct answers given. You are therefore advised to attempt all items. All items in Paper 2 will contribute to your score.

Negative marking, which used to be a feature of MCQ, caused candidates to omit a large number of items because of the fear factor. It has not been used in the MRCGP since 1992, and the reliability of the paper has improved as the number of items answered has increased. Statistical analysis has shown no evidence of random guessing! Also, new questions used to be included in the multiple choice question paper for trial purposes although such questions did not contribute to the score in that examination. However, this made it impossible to set questions based on emerging knowledge because the lead-in time of some 18 months was needed. These changes mean that all questions count to the final score.

Your must record your answers on the machine-markable sheets. If it is helpful, you may mark the question booklet as a preliminary before completing the answer sheets. If you do this, remember to leave sufficient time in which to transfer your answers. You will not be allowed extra time for this.

Make sure that on both of the answer sheets you:

- write your surname and initials in the spaces provided
- enter your candidate number in the four boxes provided and fill in the appropriate lozenge

There are separate answer sheets for the two sections of the paper which are marked separately, so make sure you fill in all the required personal information on both sheets. Figure 8.1 shows an example of how to do this.

Record your answers by making a heavy black mark that fills the lozenge completely, using only the pencil provided. If you simply mark with a faint horizontal line your answer will not be detected and you will receive no score. You may erase mistaken answers with the rubber provided. Do not complete both true and false lozenges as this will invalidate your answer!

Your answers must be recorded as follows:

For true/false questions: If you are satisfied that the answer is true, you should fill in the T lozenge; if you are satisfied that the answer is false, you should fill in the F lozenge.

Figure 8.1   *How to mark your name and examination number on the answer sheeets*

The Royal College of General Practitioners

SURNAME (Use block capitals)

INITIALS

INSTRUCTIONS	HOW TO MARK
🖎 Use black lead pencil only (HB)	Not like these:
🖎 Do NOT use ink or ballpoint pen	
🖎 Make heavy black marks that fill the lozenge completely	
🖎 Erase cleanly any answer you wish to change	But like this:
🖎 Make no stray marks on this sheet	

ENTER CANDIDATE
NUMBER HERE 🖝

NOW SHOW THE
NUMBER BY MARKING

THE GRID 🖝

🖝 Each of the 360 items on the question paper is either true or false. If you believe that the answer is true, you should fill in the T lozenge; if you believe that it is false, fill in the F lozenge. Fill in the lozenge as shown above.

🖝 Enter your answers to items 1 to 150 on this side; then turn over and continue entering your answers to items 151 to 360 on the other side.

Designed and printed by The Test Agency Ltd. Cournswood House, North Dean, High Wycombe, Bucks HP14 4NW England

133

For matching single-best-answer, multiple best answer, summary completion questions: fill in the lozenge with the letter which corresponds to your choice of answer.

No material from Paper 2 may be removed from, or copied with the intention of removing from, the examination hall. Anyone detected in attempting to do so will be deemed to have failed this paper.

Each module is marked as pass, pass with merit or fail. In May 1999, the pass rate for Paper 2 was nearly 90%. A pass in Paper 2 is approved for exemption for the purposes of the summative assessment MCQ.

Aim for a score of just over 70% and you'll pass; and if you get more than 80% you'll be on line for a merit. If you cannot score more than 65% in trial papers while preparing for the exam it suggests that your knowledge base is inadequate. So how can you ensure that your preparation is adequate?

Preparation for Paper 2

What to read

Questions can be derived from topics that cover the length and breadth of general practice. However, candidates are often concerned about the depth of knowledge that is required.

Characteristically, new items are derived from information gleaned from review articles and papers published in commonly read medical journals, primarily from the *British Medical Journal* and the *British Journal of General Practice.*

Other journals that should be studied are shown in table 8.2 (see page 135).

We would advise against the indiscriminate reading of textbooks but do recommend a problem-oriented approach in which the candidate reads up on hot topics in up-to-date text books which are at least co-authored by a GP, or review articles and consensus statements

> **Table 8.2.   *Key journals for Paper 2***
>
> British Medical Journal
> British Journal of General Practice
> Drugs and Therapeutics Bulletin
> Adverse Drug Reaction Bulletin
> Evidence Based Medicine
> Miscellaneous, including Bandolier, Effectiveness Matters, Merec
> Bulletin, etc

in the periodicals. Reading circulars from the Department of Health and the health authority/board as well as the *British Medical Journal* should keep you up to date with medicopolitical issues.

Points of technique

• Pace yourself: Start your preparation a good six months before the examination and peak at the right time. Allow about a minute an item for section 1.

• Read effectively: Review articles, evidence-based medicine and other regular journals, over the year or so prior to your examination, rather than textbooks.

• Courses: Are invaluable. Revise in a small group if possible.

• Practice: As many papers as you can lay your hands on. Use papers constructively to isolate areas of weakness. Do the phased evaluation programme (PEP)

• Answer all questions: You can mark the question paper but leave enough time to transfer your answers to the OPSCAN sheet. Remember to leave the question paper at the examination centre!

• Inspiration: If you are not sure, it is worth making an educated or inspired guess. Your initial impression is likely to be right! It may be subconscious recall.

• Jargon: Read the questions carefully and ensure that you understand the definition of conventional terms.

• OPSCAN: Use only the provided black lead HB pencil and mark the OPSCAN sheet with a heavy black mark that fills the lozenge completely. Do not complete both true and false lozenges as this will invalidate your answer.

Further information and reading

A sample Paper 2 without answers is available from RCGP Sales Department

Phased educational programme (PEP) is available from: PEP Office, Royal College of General Practitioners,12 Queen Street, Edinburgh EH2 1JE. Telephone 0131 247 3680

Greenhalgh, T. (1997) How to read a paper. In: *The basics of evidence based medicine*. London, BMJ Publishing Group.

Crombie, I.K. (1996) *The pocket guide to critical appraisal*. London, BMJ Publishing Group.

9   The Orals

Val Wass

The change to a modular format for the examination had important implications for the orals. Previously, only those who had achieved adequate marks in the written papers were allowed to proceed to the orals which were the last hurdle, whereas now the oral component can be taken at any point in the process. A full understanding of the purpose, content and structure of the orals is therefore essential to deciding when to take this module in relation to the other components, and to preparation for it.

Why have orals?

Many examination boards, particularly in North America, have abandoned orals because they are considered not to contribute significantly to the assessment process. Knowledge and skills can be effectively tested using MCQs and objective structured clinical examinations, which are more reliable tests. A viva voce examination is not thought by them to contribute over and above this to the assessment of the candidate either at postgraduate or undergraduate level.

A viva voce examination, however, remains an essential component of many British examinations and an important part of the MRCGP. After all, general practice is about daily face-to-face encounters with patients and this is the essence of the general practitioner's working life. It follows that a face-to-face encounter between candidate and examiner is a valid and important part of the assessment process for College membership. The appraisal of two-way communication at a professional level is an essential part of the admission process. It is, unashamedly, a personal encounter.

The oral must therefore be regarded as a professional interview. It is important to recognise this when taking this module of the examination. Appearances are of paramount importance. First impressions inevitably count, and formal dress is the order of the day. Both examiners and candidates should respect and value the viva-voce interaction.

What are the orals testing?

The oral module is designed so that it does not overlap with other components of the examination. Knowledge and appraisal of the medical literature, and the application of that knowledge in a general practice context, are tested in Paper 1 and need not be revisited.

Paper 2 tests factual knowledge reliably and extensively; therefore hard facts and figures need not be a part of the oral assessment because there is no point in making further judgements of knowledge base with a less effective examination tool.

What does happen in the orals is that situations are presented and clinical problems raised which the candidate is asked to discuss and appraise. The examiners then assess the candidate's ability, in the face of critical challenge, to make decisions and justify the conclusions they reach.

It is important to understand this because the essential part of the oral module is the assessment of the candidate's decision-making process. An approach by candidates which analyses options and considers the advantages and disadvantages of the possible solutions before reaching a conclusion will inevitably gain more credit than a straightforward response such as: 'In this situation, I would without hesitation do...'. The reasoning process is being examined far more than the ultimate decision.

This is where marks are to be gained. After all, in the real life of general practice there is frequently no clearly right or wrong approach to many of the situations we face, both with our patients and in the day-to day-running of a practice. Different people would inevitably solve problems in different ways, but it is the way we reach and justify our decisions that is of paramount importance, and it is this process that is being assessed.

For example, take the situation of an adolescent boy who comes to evening surgery requesting emergency contraception for his girlfriend at the crucial point 72 hours after the encounter. There are several options: refuse, consent, prescribe but insist that she comes herself, etc, and some of us would prescribe and some wouldn't. The important part of the oral assessment is the candidate's ability to identify and discuss the issues, including for instance:

- Confidentiality
- The implications of a pregnancy if contraception is not given
- Prescribing for a third party
- Ethical issues if the girlfriend is under 16 years of age
- Family planning and issues of preventive medicine

Candidates must be able to weigh up the pros and cons of the various approaches before reaching and justifying their decisions. By evaluating this process the examiners gain insight into the candidate's competence. A straightforward, rigid response: 'In no circumstances would I prescribe by proxy for a third party', is far less impressive than one which compares alternatives and makes carefully reasoned decisions. After all, emergency contraception may be readily available over the counter before too long!

How are the orals structured?

There are two oral examinations of 20 minutes' duration, each with two examiners. The second follows soon after the first, with a break of a few minutes for the candidate to rest and for the examiners to keep records and prepare for the second half. The two orals are of similar structure, covering topics that have been planned in advance by the four examiners. This planning ensures that the whole process covers a fair range of general practice subjects, and that there is no repetition or overlap between the issues covered.

In each oral four or five topics are discussed. When planning each oral, examiners have no knowledge of the candidate's marks in the other modules, nor of their video assessment; nor indeed whether these modules have been taken. They cannot link their questions to the candidate's previous performance in any way. Thus the candidate will gain four individual and independent contributions to the final mark during the course of the two parts of the orals. Experience shows that the marks can differ significantly between the two orals, mostly because of the different topics covered. Therefore candidates are well advised to use the break between them to relax, restore their composure if it has been ruffled and, by putting the previous experience behind them, approach the second oral with renewed vigour.

After each pair of orals, the four examiners meet to assess the candidate's marks and reach a final pass/fail decision. The marks given individually by each examiner are not adjusted at this point, but the achievement of borderline candidates can be reviewed in the light of the topics covered and the range of grades given. Decisions can then be made about the outcome, for instance to pass rather than fail.

What is the content of the orals?

Psychometric analysis shows that it is important to test candidates' clinical abilities in a wide and well-planned range of clinical situations (Turnbull, et al 1996). As discussed in previous chapters, the examination, including the oral module, is carefully blueprinted to ensure full coverage of relevant matters without overlapping the other modules. No one's skills are uniformly good in all situations, that is to say everyone is good at some things and not so good at others. Therefore, if weak areas are exposed in an oral every opportunity is given to candidates to perform in other contexts where they may reveal strengths. The examiners therefore plan the content of two parts of the oral together and as a whole, and create a fair examination by covering a wide a range of topics without repetition.

To do this a grid structure has been designed. Three areas of competence have been identified in which to assess the candidates' decision-making skills. It is these skills which are the focus of attention in the orals.

The areas of competence are:

- Communication
- Professional values
- Personal and professional growth

The panel of examiners has defined the attributes which successful candidates should be able to demonstrate in each area of competence, which are shown in figure 9.1.

***

Figure 9.1:   *Areas of competence which are assessed in the orals*

Communication
  Verbal and non-verbal communication generally
  Principles of communication; consultation models
  Effective information transfer; motivation
  Empathy, listening

Professional values
  General moral and ethical issues
  Patient autonomy
  Medico-legal issues
  Flexibility and tolerance
  Implications of style of practice
  Roles of health professionals
  Cultural and social factors

Personal and professional growth
  Continuing professional development
  Self-appraisal and evaluation
  Stress awareness and management: burnout
  Change and change management

***

In order to focus and achieve a wide sample of questions each of these three areas of competence is tested in four contexts relevant to general practice:

- Care of patients, specifically
- Working with colleagues (PHCT and beyond)

- Society as a whole
- Taking personal responsibility (for care, decisions and outcomes)

Questions testing each area of competence focus on one of these four contexts. Candidates should be aware of this structure because when phrasing a question an examiner may indicate the area in which he or she plans to assess the answer. For example take the topic of asthma, which can clearly be used to focus questions in many different ways. The examiner may say (example 1):

'I would like to ask you a question looking at your communication skills. How you would explain to an 18-year-old patient that he has asthma?'

In answering this candidates should focus on how they would use their communication skills with an individual patient in this age group. This question is not about asthma but about explanation, though clearly a knowledge of asthma is necessary to answer it well. It asks, 'How will you decide what to say and how to say it to this person?'.

Or the examiner may say (example 2):

I would like to ask you a question that focuses on your own personal development. You are concerned that you are becoming de-skilled in managing asthma since your partner took on responsibility for managing the practice asthma clinic. What could you do about this?'

This question is entirely focused on the candidate's individual personal development should be answered at a personal level.

Alternatively the examiner may outline a situation and ask you to discuss the issues it raises, thus (example 3):

'I would like you to consider a situation and how it might affect your professional values as a member of a practice team. It is clear from your PACT figures that asthma-prescribing costs have

significantly increased over the past six months. Your practice manager points out that the nurse running the asthma clinic sees one of the sales representatives regularly and appears to be changing patients to an expensive new inhaler. What issues does this raise for you as a team?'

The approach to answering the last example should be entirely different from the others, concentrating on matters which need addressing in managing a disease such as asthma, concerning attitudes and values within a multi-professional team.

Figure 9.2 represents the grid in which competence and context can be related to each other in devising questions and planning an oral. It is used to ensure full coverage of the areas of competence and the contexts within them, and shows where these three example questions focus. Thus in figure 9.2 the questions above correspond to the areas indicated by Q1, Q2 and Q3.

Figure 9.2:   *Relationship of areas of competence to context*

How the three example questions are placed

Context	Areas of competence		
	Communication	Professional values	Personal and professional growth
Care of patients	Example question 1	N/A	N/A
Working with colleagues	N/A	Example question 3	N/A
Society	N/A	N/A	N/A
Personal responsibility	N/A	N/A	Example question 2

From the candidates' point of view it is clearly important to listen carefully to the question, clarify it if they are uncertain what is being asked, and keep to the area in which the question has been focused. If it is an area in which they know very little and are performing poorly, they should say so and enable the examiners to move on to the next question where performance may be significantly better. Don't flog a lost cause — move on to hopefully greener pastures!

How is the oral planned?

The two pairs of examiners plan the oral in the competence-context grid structure described above, to ensure that over the two orals a comprehensive range of topics is covered. The candidate should be given the opportunity to demonstrate competence in all the contexts outlined above. Figure 9.3 outlines a possible format for one oral.

Figure 9.3:   ***Form used for planning an oral***

	Area of competence			Context			
Topic	Communi-cation	Profess'l values	Pers'n'l and profess'l growth	Care of patients	Working with colleagues	Society	Personal respons-ibility
1 PHCT	—	X	—	—	X	—	—
2 Breaking bad news	X	—	—	X	—	—	—
3 Reaccre-ditation	—	—	X	—	—	—	X
4 Access to medical records	—	X	—	—	—	X	—
5 Burnout in a colleague	X	—	—	—	X	—	—

During planning the questions are listed on the left under 'Topic', and as the oral proceeds a cross or tick is placed against the area of competence and the context in which the topic has been examined.

The questions in this oral might be:

1 What makes an effective primary health care team?

From this stem the examiner could explore with the candidates the professional values on which they base team management and their ability to assess how a team is functioning.

2 What communication principles would you use in breaking bad news to a patient?

The examiner would explore the candidates' understanding of communication principles and how they are used in breaking bad news. They could also further explore that ability by applying it to a specific case, or in relation to consultation models.

3 Revalidation is under consideration and will almost inevitably be introduced during your future career as a general practitioner. Would you personally be in favour of the process?

The candidates' perception of themselves, as individuals, would be explored and the implications for their own development discussed.

4 How might you respond if a patient's employer asked you to release his medical records for the perusal of the company's medical officer?

This question would enable the examiner to explore the candidates' understanding of professional values and ethical principles, which can underpin management of such a request in the light of the patient's position in society. A specific scenario could be developed to illustrate this and explore it further.

5 Your health visitor reports that two patients have complained that your senior partner has the smell of alcohol on his breath in the morning baby clinic. How might you communicate your concerns to him?

The candidate would be encouraged to explore ways of using communication skills to handle sensitive issues within the practice.

Careful planning allows the oral to explore the candidate's approach to practice in as much breadth as possible. At the same time, by confining each question to specific areas within the competency-context structure, the candidate's ability can also be explored in depth.

Candidates are therefore well advised to understand and follow this structure. They should keep to the point of the individual questions to demonstrate the extent of their ability. However, they should not waste time if they find themselves in a weak area, but allow the examiner to move on to the next question so that the breadth of the oral is utilised to their advantage.

How is the oral marked?

The candidate's responses are graded against a verbal scale. There are nine potential categories ranging from 'outstanding' through 'good', 'satisfactory', and 'not adequate', to 'poor' and 'dangerous'. For example,

- To be outstanding, a candidate would have to be: 'Uniformly outstanding, well-read, coherent, rational and critical, justifying all approaches by reference to literature'
- To be judged good he or she would have to be: 'Generally impressive, well-informed, fairly critical, with good decision making skills and able to justify the majority of approaches well'
- Satisfactory grade is given to a candidate who is: 'Characterised by a reassuring solidness rather than impressiveness. Able to justify only some approaches well, but most appear sensible. Adequate, not good decision making skills'

Outstanding is clearly very unusual, and the 'dangerous' grade, which is given when the candidate's approach is 'so arbitrary as to put patients at risk', has been used very rarely.

Candidates who cannot demonstrate at least the satisfactory level of ability are considered borderline or below, and may fail.

In each oral, the examiners mark all the questions independently of each other, and at the end decide on a final overall grade for that oral, again independently of each other. Thus over the two orals, four grades are obtained which are entirely independent of performance in any of the other modules. The final mark for the oral module is then calculated from a combination of these individual grades, and results are expressed as merit, pass or fail. It follows that a spread of grading is achieved by a cohort of candidates with the mean around the satisfactory level.

Flexible but discriminating questions

Examiners generally use a limited bank of questions which are well standardised, that is to say they have been used repeatedly over a period of time and the range and type of response has been well tested. The examiners lead the introduction of topics in turn, while the other examiner records an independent judgement of the candidate's response, controlling that a fair assessment has been achieved. The marks are not averages; however, experience and statistics confirm that it is in the candidate's interest to maintain individual examiner judgements.

It is important for both examiners and candidates to recognise that each question must be structured in a way that will test a range of responses. It must enable the examiner to make a decision at the pass/fail level but at the same time have the capacity to test a candidate at the excellent/outstanding level. Recognition of this from the candidate's point of view is important for two reasons.

First, as each question proceeds it will get progressively more difficult and almost inevitably, if they are being examined well, candidates will find there is a point beyond which they cannot deliver information. Thus they have reached their own personal level on the calibration grade, although they will have no idea of this beyond an uncomfortable feeling that they have not been able to stretch their answer to match the examiner's probing. Excellent candidates, when stretched to the limit, may well feel they are performing poorly. This cannot be avoided; it is an examination. It is crucial to come to terms with this feeling and not panic! It is intrinsic to the examination process.

Similarly, it may be equally difficult for a candidate at the pass/fail level to gauge his performance in the absence of any feedback from the examiners. The key to this is to take every question as it comes, approach each new one afresh and recognise that discomfort may be an inevitable part of the process. Although the overall advice is to approach the oral as a professional interview with examiners who are trained to make every effort to make the candidate feel welcomed and at ease, discomfort and uncertainty in an examination cannot be avoided.

Secondly, it is important to recognise that, as the examiner progressively challenges the candidate in order to calibrate the reply, strategies for increasing the difficulty of the question will be used. Factual knowledge is not being tested, but inevitably the better candidate will be able to quote and appraise evidence from the literature to justify the response given. Similarly the examiner may create progressively more difficult scenarios to explore depth of understanding of ethical principles.

How best to prepare for the examination?

Although the oral does not specifically test the candidate's factual knowledge and foundation for the evidence-based practice of medicine, obviously the process of decision making and justification cannot take place without it. A background of knowledge and awareness of the literature with which to justify approaches and decisions is clearly essential, as is experience of practice. Inevitably therefore the oral is best approached towards the end of vocational training when sufficient experience has been gained.

It is important, therefore, to keep up to date and remain engaged in active practice as much as possible. Working in pairs or small groups for the orals can be stimulating. A good exercise is to devise questions, using the competence context system, and the process of seeking ways to increase the difficulty of each question can be very educational. Active role play in preparation for the examination is to be encouraged. Almost every surgery session has one consultation or associated event from which a question could be devised. Practice can be very helpful.

The examiners are practising general practitioners who come from all over the United Kingdom, and a full understanding of the range and variety of all aspects of British general practice is crucial. The candidate's own area of practice will not be the focus of questions; rather, the examiners will expect a broad understanding of all kinds of practice. For example, a candidate with experience of inner-city work could be asked about the problems of rural practice, or someone whose work involves many elderly patients questions about the care of children.

What happens on the day?

As stressed above, it is important to treat the event as one would approach any professional interview. Dress smartly, and allow plenty of time for travel so that you arrived relaxed. Before each round of orals starts the candidates are briefed about the arrangements of the examination by the examiner marshal covering the day, which takes several minutes, so it's not a good idea to arrive at the very last moment.

Candidates are not allocated to examiners from their own region of practice and should not be examined by anyone they know personally, for obvious reasons. As the number of MRCGP courses throughout the UK increases, the situation occasionally arises where a candidate has met the examiner before. If the candidate recognises an examiner and would prefer not to be examined by that person, a clear statement should be made immediately so that substitution can be arranged.

Sometimes a third person may be present at the examination, as an observer. He or she may be a visitor from another medical faculty or profession, attending to share and develop ideas for their own examination procedures. Also general practitioners interested in becoming examiners themselves observe for two days as part of the specially designed selection process, before attending for the later stages of selection. Experienced examiners may also observe for training purposes (Wakeford et al 1995). Candidates should ignore any observers, as they do not contribute to the oral examination or its marking at all. They are there only to study the examination process.

Occasionally candidates may find that a video camera is recording the oral for examiner training purposes. As with observers, this is part of the training and development processes of the exam. Candidates can be reassured that only the examiners appear on the screen and the recording is only used for feedback to the examiners concerned and for teaching purposes within the panel of examiners.

Every effort is made to ensure a smooth and efficient procedure, though it is recognised that any oral examination inevitably has its own intrinsic stress for the candidate. Careful preparation for the orals can reduce this stress and enhance performance. A full understanding of the structure and procedures as outlined here provides a useful basis on which to prepare. A series of example questions can be found in appendix 6, which illustrates the type of question which may be found in each area of the competency-context grid. Readers are encouraged to study these examples and formulate answers to them appropriate to their places in the grid, to enhance their understanding of the different emphasis to be found in each of the twelve areas.

References

Turnbull J, Danoff D, Norman G (1996) Content specificity and oral certification examinations. *Medical Education*, 30, 56-59.

Wakeford R, Southgate L, Wass V (1995) Improving oral examinations: selecting, training and monitoring examiners for the MRCGP. *British Medical Journal*, 311, 931-935.

10 Membership by assessment of performance

The development of a method for assessing established general practitioners

Iona Heath and John Holden

The MRCGP examination, excellent though it undoubtedly is, has for many years been taken largely by young doctors at the start of their careers in general practice. This chapter describes the development of a method for assessing established general practitioners. For such experienced GPs, whether principals or not, the prospect of a formal examination must seem so daunting that few choose to take it. Until now the exam has been the only normal route to membership, so the College has effectively either recruited young GPs or lost them forever. Although numbers of members increased substantially during the 1970s and 1980s, the last decade has seen a levelling of membership numbers which has left nearly half the profession outside the College. This has been repeatedly lamented, but a solution has not been forthcoming.

In 1991 the College Council agreed to consider introducing a system of membership by assessment for established practitioners (RCGP 1991). Doubts expressed by faculties led to delay in pursuing this idea, but a survey showing a demand for such a scheme (Baker and Pringle 1995) led to the College Council creating a working group charged with exploring the possibilities for membership by assessment of performance (MAP) further. This has now become a new route to membership of the RCGP, and the first candidates are expected to be assessed in late 1999-early 2000. We summarise the process by which this scheme was developed and discuss some of the purposes it may fulfil.

The basis for this method of development

MAP had to meet several requirements. It had to be of equivalent standard to the MRCGP examination so that neither could be considered a softer option, with members by either route being of equal status. It needed to assess important aspects of the daily work of GPs so that it had credibility with the profession and wider public rather than being narrowly academic. The method of assessment had to be open to consistent interpretation by candidates and assessors so that candidates knew in advance what to expect, and different assessors would reach the same conclusions were they to assess the same candidate. Finally, we had to develop a method to assess GPs working in a wide variety of circumstances, both demographic and personal (eg both principals and non-principals, full and part-time).

In brief, whereas the MRCGP examination aims to test what candidates can do, that is to say it is a test of competence, MAP aims to test what they actually do, ie it is a test of performance. The two methods have the same test of consulting skills by means of either a video of consultations, or a simulated surgery.

Doctors, patients, managers and the government all have views on the importance of the different parts of a GP's work. As a route to membership of a professional organisation we considered it appropriate to restrict our collection of views to practising GPs, yet from a wide variety of settings.

It is desirable that a method of assessment should be open and consistent in order to be seen to be just. We needed to produce a scheme that would be published in full so that potential candidates would know in advance exactly what is expected of them, and which would be assessed consistently on differing occasions. These were demanding and potentially labour-intensive criteria and we therefore had to consider whether we could adapt an existing scheme for our purpose.

Our immediate choice was fellowship of the RCGP by assessment (RCGP 1990). This started in 1989 for those seeking to demonstrate the highest possible standards of practice. If we had reduced the requirement to examine a number of new cases of cancer from 15 to, say, eight, this might have been feasible for some criteria. However others, such as the requirement to have adequate emergency drugs and equipment, are not amenable to a lower standard so we abandoned this option.

The expert group guiding the development of MAP knew of no other existing set of standards of performance by general practitioners that could be used or adapted to our purpose. We therefore decided to carry out our own consultation exercise with a wide cross section of the profession in order to determine the criteria upon which to base MAP.

Consulting the profession

We identified a wide variety of GPs from organisations representing general practitioners (table 10.1 below).

Table 10.1:   *The groups that took part in the study*

- Associate members of the RCGP (excluding GP registrars)
- Association of University Teachers in General Practice members
- Fellows of the RCGP by assessment
- MRCGP candidates who passed the exam in 1996
- MRCGP examiners
- Overseas Doctors Association members
- RCGP Council members
- RCGP members who passed the exam before 1992
- Small Practices Association members

Each was asked to supply the names of 60 of their members chosen at random, all of whom were sent an explanation of the study and an invitation to participate. Volunteers were required to be in active general practice and expecting to remain so for the next year. From the names supplied, we selected, at random, 20 people from each group to take part.

To consult such a large number of individuals we chose a Delphi technique (Cantrill et al 1996). These are useful for developing standards when there is insufficient research based evidence in the area. They ask a group of people the same questions, and feedback amalgamated answers through a series of two or more stages. They have the advantages of overcoming geographical separation and interpersonal conflicts between participants, and excessive deference to experts, and they have been used in previous consultation exercises with general practitioners (Hutchinson and Fowler 1992, Munro et al 1998).

Each participant was sent instructions explaining the study and asking them to suggest aspects of a GP's performance that are important to assess. They were told that it did not matter if they did not know how an aspect of performance might be assessed; if they thought it important they were to include it. We gave 12 separate areas of practice as aides memoires, collated from previous work on the quality of general practice (Pendleton et al 1986, Toon 1994, GMC 1998, RCGP 1995) and not in any order of importance. Respondents were asked to write brief phrases or sentences and to reply within three weeks, with reminders being sent to non-responders.

We recruited 175 GPs to take part in the study from the target of 180, and 91 (52%), sent in replies to the first round. All replies (65 000 words) were transcribed on to a spreadsheet and each was independently checked and categorised into one of the 12 areas of practice, retaining all responses. A group of four GPs from Mersey faculty then read through all the responses in each area and produced 113 new statements to encompass the views expressed in the first round.

They were asked to produce about 10 statements in each area since we wanted the second Delphi round to be of reasonable length yet comprehensive and specific. These statements were then sent back to the Delphi group asking them to number each statement, as aspects of performance, either: 2 – essential; 1 – desirable; 0 – unnecessary. Additional opinions were invited as free text comments. 128 (73%) replied to the second round.

Producing and piloting a draft document

We invited all those who had taken part in the Delphi study; representatives of the General Medical Council and British Medical

Association; and the profession in general by means of an advertisement in the *British Journal of General Practice* to a conference in January 1998. The main purpose of the event was to translate the results of the Delphi rounds into assessable criteria for MAP. Sixty participants considered four areas of practice in facilitated small groups, with each area being covered by two different groups. The delegates were given a set of all results from the Delphi and asked to stay close to the collective views from that consultation.

The different criteria produced by the conference were incorporated into a draft document which was reviewed with two potential MAP candidates. Their task was not to complete a full MAP assessment but to produce the sort of evidence they would use to support an application, and to identify statements that were difficult to interpret. We then tested the full draft scheme with four more pilot candidates in May 1998. They submitted evidence in advance and were visited by two assessors who interviewed them and their staff, examined records and conducted an assessment that was as near as possible to the full scheme, again constrained by the short time the candidates had available to prepare.

Experience gained from these visits enabled us to submit a scheme for membership by assessment of performance to the RCGP Council in June 1998. The Council recommended that this be submitted to the annual general meeting as a proposal for a change in College ordinances allowing this new route to membership. Three further pilot assessments were undertaken in the autumn of 1998. Ten revisions of the draft MAP document were considered by the faculty and national MAP working groups in 1998, each allowing minor refinements to make the scheme as clear as possible. The annual general meeting adopted membership by assessment of performance as a new route to membership of the College in November, and after Privy Council approval MAP became available in April 1999.

Discussion

Many of the respondents to the Delphi consultation belonged to more than one professional group, often three or four. For that reason we did not analyse the results by different professional categories. Although we tried to consult as wide a cross-section of the profession as we could, we depended upon professional associations being able to give us lists of names of members, and the proportion of their members this represented varied with their size. They represent a cross-section of the profession, but not one weighted for all variables since Delphi panels typically include a disproportionate number of enthusiasts (Cantrill et al).

The process of converting the initial replies into a schedule that could be marked could have resulted in some proposals being ambiguous, or a statement that might be agreed with only in part. For example, participants might agree that a candidate should keep up to date with chronic disease management, but a learning portfolio might not be an appropriate way to demonstrate this, or they might consider this unintelligible jargon.

We had to condense a considerable amount of initial data into the series for the second round and we have retained all the original replies for future reference. The respondents apparently had little difficulty in suggesting aspects of GPs' performance that should be assessed in a scheme such as this. This probably reflects a growing awareness of professional assessment as a whole and possible individual components of it.

Delphi techniques can be used to substantially increase a group's capacity to generate ideas. Various modifications are possible depending upon the purpose of the study, and in this case we needed to know the range of performance measures the profession thought important, and have some indication of the level of support for each.

There was no commitment to include any individual criterion in the MAP scheme, although all involved in its development have tried to be faithful to the Delphi group's ideas and opinions. We did not attempt to reach any pre-determined level of consensus. The full results of the Delphi consultation have been published in the *British Journal of General Practice* in order to give everyone an opportunity to judge how far the MAP criteria are based on the views of the profession expressed in this exercise (Holden J and Wearne J, 2000).

The highest scoring criteria are shown in table 10.2 below. They reflect traditional ideas of the role of the general practitioner such as availability and clinical skills as well as good practice management.

In contrast, the least favoured criteria (table 10.3, below) include some current ideas such as formularies, complementary therapies and apparently over-easy access by patients. Health promotion in general scored badly, and only one out of the 36 compulsory criteria is devoted to it.

Table 10.2.   The highest scoring criteria proposed

- Demonstrate the system for urgent problems necessitating same day appointments
- Demonstrate arrangements for care of emergency situations in and out of office hours
- Sufficient drugs and equipment should be available for the doctor to manage a variety of acute problems seen by GPs
- Records are comprehensive, legible and appropriately accessible
- The candidate's prescribing should be clinically appropriate

---

Table 10.3. The lowest scoring criteria proposed

- There should be a practice formulary in use
- The practice has written information for patients and guidelines on common acute illness
- Practice has a published policy on waiting times
- The candidate should describe and justify their use of complementary therapies
- Doctor is available when patients decide they need to consult

As far as possible we were concerned to develop a system of assessment that concentrates upon the performance of the individual GP irrespective of the practice or primary care groups within which they are working. We believe this system will compliment performance indicators for primary care groups, which will be developed separately (McColl et al 1998). Our pilot visits included full and part-time practitioners, GPs in partnerships and those who are single handed. No doubt some circumstances have been overlooked. but the annual review of the criteria will give us the opportunity to take these into account.

The Council of the RCGP has approved the principles of MAP, which are:

1 MAP is by self-nomination by general practitioners who are at least five years post-vocational training and who have worked for a minimum of three sessions a week in a general practice for the past year.

2 MAP is criterion referenced, with the criteria being reliable, reproducible and evidence based (ie assessment is made against defined criteria which are the same for all candidates).

3 There is one level of pass.

4 All the essential criteria in MAP, and a proportion of the non-essential criteria, must be achieved.

5 The criteria are based on care for patients in a general practice in those dimensions considered important by the membership and others consulted.

6 The criteria are published and openly available.

7 The criteria are reviewed and updated each year, with approval resting with the College Council.

8 The assessment is undertaken by members of the RCGP.

9 Membership by assessment of performance has equivalence to membership by examination.

There are now a number of quality assurance schemes for general practice (Spooner and Holden 1997). MAP is unique in being developed from a consultation process with a wide section of the profession. It remains to be seen whether this will ensure its credibility and popularity.

Why do MAP?

First and foremost candidates must want to become members of the RCGP. MAP and the MRCGP examination are the only ways of joining the RCGP, and all College members must wish that their non-members colleagues would join them in order to strengthen the profession in its primary purpose of advancing patient care. Undertaking MAP is not an endorsement of everything the College has done or will do, but a powerful statement of the value candidates place on professional unity rather than division.

The opportunity to prove to one's peers that patients are being well cared for will be a major factor for many. Although more and more routinely collected data about our performance is available, this still gives only a partial picture of the quality of care patients are receiving. MAP attempts to be comprehensive since candidates must perform well across all the major areas of practice and none can be neglected. Indeed no-one has suggested to us that MAP is easy, quite the contrary.

The assessors will strive to be fair. As practising general practitioners themselves they will realise that perfect practice is impossible. Yet they will be thorough, and read the whole lengthy submission and ask some searching questions, usually in the nicest possible way! They know that most of the hard work will have been done prior to the assessment visit which should be an opportunity for candidates to shine. However, they will also be determined that success should be earned and do not want anyone to think the visit can be taken for granted as a mere formality.

There are few other opportunities for established doctors, including GPs, to have such a searching examination by their colleagues, which should give an appropriate sense of satisfaction to those who pass. Incidentally, we have no pre-determined pass rate: if all candidates fulfil the criteria, which we hope they will do, we shall be delighted with a 100% pass rate. In turn, we believe that success in MAP will encourage the striving to do even better for patients in future. This may be easier to achieve when one has a realistic understanding of where one is at the present time.

Professional revalidation, clinical governance, primary care groups, and practice professional development plans are all new terms which have appeared within the past few years which we are gradually starting to understand. Each is concerned in different ways with the performance of people working in the health service, including general practitioners. At the present time MAP is a far more demanding undertaking than anything required by the new schemes.

Although at the time of writing (autumn 1999) we still do not know whether working towards MAP, or completing it, will automatically exempt doctors from the demands of the other innovations, it seems likely that it will do so. Indeed, we hope many GPs will want to demonstrate that they practice to a high standard rather than a bare minimum.

Local support

RCGP faculties throughout Britain are identifying members who will be able, in time, to advise and support MAP candidates. Indeed, experience shows that peer support in small groups is often a vital part of preparation for an undertaking such as MAP. Enthusiasm invariably waxes and wanes and voluntary accountability to others may well help in the leaner times when there are just so many more things to do.

Advisers must be able to encourage potential candidates while trying to ensure that they present themselves for assessment only when they have reached the necessary standard.

Faculties in turn can ask the national MAP implementation group for help and advice. This group is keen to promote MAP, but also to adapt it as experience is gained and we understand more about the assessment of mature doctors. We make no apologies for wanting as many fellow GPs as possible to become College members, and we hope MAP will prove an excellent introduction. It must be rooted in what good GPs are doing in practice, change as knowledge and practice advance, yet remain a peer-assessment that the profession as a whole can be satisfied with.

It is too early to count numbers, but a key element in the assessment of the quality of MAP itself will be the success it achieves in encouraging GPs to undertake it. Although some early candidates may be under pressure to take MAP for career reasons, it will be the informal opinion of colleagues that will influence most to take, or not take, MAP.

References

Baker M, Pringle M (1995) Membership of the Royal College of General Practitioners by assessment: attitudes of members and non-members in one faculty area. *British Journal of General Practice* 45: 405–407.

Cantrill JA, Sibbald B, Buetow S (1996). The Delphi and nominal group techniques in health services research. *International Journal of Pharmaceutical Practice* 4: 67–74.

General Medical Council (1998). *Good Medical Practice*. London, GMC.

Holden J, Wearne J (2000) Membership by Assessment of Performance: developing a method of assessing established general practitioners. *British Journal of General Practice* 50, 231–235.

Hutchinson A, Fowler P (1992). Outcome measures for primary care: what are the research priorities? *British Journal of General Practice* 42: 227–231.

McColl A, Roderick P, Gabbay J, Smith H, Moore M (1998). Performance indicators for primary care groups: an evidence-based approach. *British Medical Journal* 317: 1354-60.

Munro N, Hornung R, McAleer S (1998). What are the key attributes of a good general practice trainer? A Delphi study. *Education for General Practice* 9: 263-270.

Pendleton D, Schofield T, Marinker M (1986). *In pursuit of quality*. London, RCGP.

Royal College of General Practitioners (1990). Fellowship by assessment. *Occasional paper 50*. London, RCGP.

Royal College of General Practitioners (1991) *Members' Reference Book*. London, RCGP.

Royal College of General Practitioners (1995). *The nature of general medical practice*. London, RCGP.

Spooner A, Holden J. 1997. The major quality assurance schemes for general practice. *Primary Care* 7: 7–10.

Toon PD (1994). What is good medical practice? *Occasional Paper 65*. London, RCGP.

11   Preparing a MAP application

Iona Heath and John Wearne

Membership by assessment of performance is attainable by the majority of practising general practitioners, but it is an undertaking that can be completed only with considerable planning and forethought. The criteria have been determined by the profession and encompass subject areas that were considered to describe the important aspects of the work that we all do on a daily basis.

Membership by assessment has been designed to be accessible not only to full-time principals in general practice but also to part-time principals, retainer scheme doctors, assistants and locums. It is important to remember that gaining membership of the Royal College of General Practitioners is only one outcome of this process. Perhaps a more valuable outcome is an improved ability to provide quality care to your practice population.

The criteria for assessment

For an application to be accepted there are two eligibility criteria that have to be attained:

- UK independent practice (ie GP vocationally trained) for five years
- Work a minimum of three sessions a week in a single practice for one year.

It would be difficult to gain the evidence required if these criteria were not met, hence their necessity. There will be some rare circumstances that will need to be considered by the chairman of the MAP implementation group and in these cases referral to the MAP office is advised. The process of application and assessment is described in detail in the MAP Handbook (RCGP 1999). It contains all the criteria that have to be gained, and a wealth of ideas that can be used for general quality improvements. Before you start planning your application it is important to read through the entire document. It is laid out with the criteria that have to be met on the left hand page, with the corresponding evidence that has to be produced placed directly opposite on the right hand side. In some cases there are examples of how evidence should be submitted. Although the format is not compulsory the nature of the required evidence is. On the both sides of the handbook it is clearly shown which criteria are essential and which are optional. All essential criteria have to be passed, requiring all the specified evidence to be submitted. A number of the optional criteria also have to be gained, the exact number of which is detailed in the handbook and can vary from year to year along with the criteria themselves.

Finally, on the right hand side it is clearly shown which criteria have to be submitted in advance. The assessors will have read all of your submission in detail before the assessment day but this does not preclude your being questioned on any area. All criteria may be examined in some detail, including how the information was gathered, and in some of the criteria, the outcomes in terms of patient benefit.

Making a start

Most people will take nine to 12 months to complete the entire preparation, and this is then followed by the assessment visit. Each faculty area has at least one adviser as well as members or Fellows of the college who have received further training in assessment techniques. It is advisable to make contact with an adviser early in the application process for guidance with the planning. Your local faculty office administrative assistant, or the RCGP central office in London on 020 7581 3232, will be able to supply their names and telephone numbers.

Much can be prepared in advance, and it is worth organising this at an early stage:

1 CPR certificate: The criteria for this are the same as MRCGP by examination, and it needs to be organised in advance. Once you have gained certification it is valid for three years.

2   Child health certificate, or evidence that you are on your health authority's child health surveillance list. It may be valuable to discuss your personal circumstance with your faculty mentor regarding child health surveillance. There is no requirement to have been on a specific training course.

3   Consulting skills assessment is the same as the procedures for the MRCGP exam described in chapters 5 and 6. MAP candidates may choose either video or simulated surgery, but the option of simulated surgery requires an additional fee to reflect the extra expense involved. For many people, this part of the assessment is a significant concern, though there is usually no need to worry. The vast majority of practising general practitioners are consulting to the standard required to pass. It is entirely understandable if video consultation analysis is new to you, or you have not been used to surgeries being recorded, but there will be people locally who have been, and regularly undergo video analysis. Your local adviser can put you in touch with someone with experience or help you join a group preparing for MAP. Again, once the video has been submitted and passed by the examination panel, the approval lasts for three years.

4   Audits: this is a term that engenders a love-hate response from GPs. You are probably participating in personal and practice audits already, though it is important to document the work being undertaken to use as a basis for your application. Such work can also count towards your practice professional development plan.

It is then important to plan your preparations. Some criteria will take much more work than others; some are very short, others long. Look at the handbook carefully, decide which areas can be tackled fairly easily and make your plans for the more time-consuming ones.

The application

The application process is detailed in the handbook. The initial evidence required includes:

- CPR certificate in date
- Certificate of competence in child health

• Current GMC or Medical Council of Ireland registration.
• Confirmation of eligibility as outlined in paragraph 2 of this chapter
• Current application fee

On receipt of this evidence by the MAP office you will be sent a video workbook, a list of the current criteria and a date by which evidence must be submitted. The MAP implementation group intends to re-assess the criteria continually in the light of current best practice and feedback from candidates and assessors. There will therefore be annual revisions of the MAP handbook. If you miss the date you have been given you will be assessed on the next version of the MAP criteria. Make sure you have the latest edition.

The ten areas

There are 10 areas of performance that comprise the basis of the assessment of performance, shown in table 11.1 below.

Table 11.1:   *The 10 areas to be assessed*

1   Accessibility and continuity

2   Continued professional development/review of performance

3   Ethical standards

4   Health promotion

5   Management of acute illness

6   Management of chronic illness

7   Patient records

8   Practice organisation and team working

9   Prescribing and referral

10 Consultation

---

1 Accessibility and continuity

In the development of MAP the doctors involved rated this area of performance as one of the most important. It is factual, and will be checked by the assessors on the day. It is an area that can involve some work for reception staff, and they should be briefed that on the day of assessment they may well be questioned about the data presented. For example, it may be advisable that the reception staff has available a list of those things that the practice considers require an urgent appointment. It will be necessary to demonstrate how a request for an urgent visit is processed, as is shown in example 11.1. Tables of how this and other data may be presented are available in the MAP handbook.

Example 11.1

Emergencies include:

Breathing difficulties   Chest pain   Cerebrovascular events

Collapse   Bleeding   Second calls

Calls regarding children, particularly breathing difficulties, conscious level change, and children under 1 year old.

At the assessment visit, the staff may well be asked to present the appointment system and show when the next available appointment with the candidate is. If this does not tally with the evidence presented, an explanation of circumstances leading to such a discrepancy will be expected.

It is important in 1(c) that only direct consultation time is counted. It is not acceptable to include time between consultations. Area 1(e) is concerned with continuity and it may be a topic for discussion on the assessment day, too, if there seems to be little continuity in the care of an individual patient. For example, if in the investigation or follow up of a particular complaint, the patient often sees more than one doctor, the assessors may wish to discuss the topic in more depth. There may, of course, be valid explanations for such occurrences.

2 Continued professional development/review of performance

Although MAP has been developed to assess an individual doctor's performance there are some areas in which practice work may be reflected. This is not the case in area 2 which is very much personal. The intention is to review the identification of educational needs, how those needs were met and the changes to practice that occurred as a result. Identification may be from an individual patient problem or question; at this point the use of a reflective diary or educational prescription may be demonstrated. The need may not be one of a clinical nature, it could relate to a managerial or personal issue.

Whatever is chosen they should be of a substantial nature and an explanation of the choice is required. It will normally be considered insufficient to state that your educational needs are met from a weekly trip to the postgraduate meeting. Demonstration of reading peer reviewed journals is expected and a log of involvement in any teaching to registrars/medical or paramedical staff should be kept.

Area 2 has three optional sections (with a maximum of four points in MAP version 1). In 2(e) there are a maximum of three points available from four areas. On each of these it is important to describe why this was chosen, what you did and what was the outcome. 2(f) is concerned with the use of a reflective diary, and you could gain a point here by expanding on the diary you have kept to identify your educational needs. In this section to gain a point the improvement in patient care that this diary brought about must also be demonstrated. In 2(g) it is expected that a short commentary accompanies each event, as in example 11.2.

Example 11.2 Cerebrovascular accident in a patient under 65

Male age 42, reference 4694

Past medical history

1995   Smoker 40 cigarettes per day

1997   Stopped smoking, overweight. Referred to dietitian at work

1997	Vasectomy

April 98   Letter received. While working in Italy, suffered an episode which may have been a CVA. He gave a history of weakness in his right arm which spread to his right leg. Also noticed a loss of control and coordination of his hand and upper limb. The symptoms settled over one week. Blood pressure readings back to 1992 have always been borderline at around 150/90, fasting lipids normal. Now smoking again 10-12 per day. Referred to neurologist. Started on aspirin.

June 98   Letter received, BP noted at 148/98, right sided reflexes enhanced slightly. Thought possibly to have had lacuna stroke, due to hypertension.

Aug 99   MRI scan shows lacuna infarct, otherwise investigations normal. R. nifedipine CR 30mg bd. Fasting cholesterol 5.8 mmol/l

Comment

This gentleman suffered a CVA while abroad. He has been known to have some risk factors namely, overweight and smoking, along with a BP being at the higher end of the normal range. Despite these factors having been identified and advice arranged for him, he still suffered a CVA. He was referred urgently to a neurologist, and aspirin was started immediately, so I feel that all that was necessary was done initially. His BP has been difficult to control but he is being seen regularly. Unfortunately he is still smoking, and does not seem to appreciate the potential severity of his condition. His weight is still considerably raised at 100kg, a BMI of 32. Perhaps treatment should have been instituted at an earlier date.

3 Ethical standards

This area is concerned with ensuring that your practice is in accordance with the GMC guideline booklet *Good Medical*

Practice. It is advisable to read this booklet and ensure that you comply with all the issues involved. Under 3(a) and (c) the assessors may wish to discuss such issues with reception staff and the practice manager on the day of the assessment. The remainder will be discussed with the candidate.

4 Health promotion

It is intended in this short area that you demonstrate you have undertaken a brief audit in a subject that has local relevance. It is not necessary here to reproduce an in-depth study, a short summary of findings will be sufficient. It is expected that the audit will be prospective. Again demonstration of change within the practice will be expected to have occurred, as in example 11.3.

Example 11.3   Coronary bypass follow-up audit

Aim: to ensure that all patients who have had a CABG:

• Are on aspirin or warfarin
• Have had a fasting lipid measurement within the last two years
• If fasting lipids >5mmol are on cholesterol lowering therapy
First audit March 1999. Six months remedial action. Second audit September 1999.

Coronary bypass follow up results					
Date	Number in group	Number had lipid test <2 years	Number on treatment	Number with latest cholesterol<5	Number on aspirin or warfarin
3/99	15	10	9	8	8
9/99	17	17	12	13	17

Comment

I feel that we have shown great improvement in this audit. Our next aim will be to reduce further the number with cholesterol levels greater than 5 mmol/l. We now have a group of patients who have had a CABG on the computer which we re-check every 6 months. I would like to be able to show an outcome of a lowering of morbidity here, however I would need a much larger group and need to follow them over a number of years.

5 Management of acute illness

This and the following sections constitute a significant proportion of the clinical performance assessment. The assessors will wish to corroborate your submission with evidence from your personal records. A list of your emergency drugs must be submitted. It is advisable to review them a week or so prior to the visit as it is an area that assessors can easily check. 5(c) involves presenting 20 acute cases. A suggested format is shown in the MAP handbook with examples. It is important that the patients are identified only by a number. The assessors will wish to discuss some of these cases with you and the patients' notes will be required at that time. In 5(d) one case will be discussed at the visit to check on the details of the case management. Again, it is necessary that the notes are readily available for these cases, preferably already collated. It might be presented as in example 11.4.

Example 11.4   Emergency admission for asthma

Male, aged 2 years 1 month at time of admission. Reference 0514

Past medical history

Sept 96	Normal birth
June 97	Crying all day, seen out of hours
Aug 97	Cough, wheeze, seen out of hours
April 98	Self-referral to hospital. Diagnosis of asthma. Required prednisolone and salbutamol. Parents took him home against advice.
April 98	Surgery appointment, R. salbutamol nebules, nebuliser loaned.

Sept 98	Seen at home, very wheezy. Hospital admission. Required nebuliser and oral steroids. Discharged on salbutamol/beclomethasone via spacer device.
Nov 98	Hospital follow up appointment, keeping well on above therapy.
Jan 99	Further admission with asthma secondary to URTI. Self-discharge on 20/1/99. Followed up by health visitor.

Comment

This young child has developed asthma at a very early age. We may well continue to have problems here with regard to health education advice. Control of his condition I feel may be erratic as the home circumstances are far from ideal. His father smokes although his mum does not. There are four other children. The father is 25 years old and the mother 28. One brother born in 1994 also has asthma, and there is another brother born in 1995 who has had meningococcal meningitis this year. It will be necessary to ensure that he does not default from paediatric OPD follow up. The health visitors are fully aware of the condition and the family.

The optional parts of area 5 are (e) and (f); (e) builds on the format in 5(d), while 5(f) requires that the patient or relatives of someone with the condition have commented on each of the information leaflets.

6 Management of chronic illness

This is the second clinical area. It will require reviewing the processes you already have established, checking them against current best practice, and many candidates will need to ensure their team members are involved.

In 6(a) a management plan is required, based on current best practice for three of the listed areas. The plans and documented source(s) for the guidelines will be discussed with the candidate at the visit. 6(b) requires three prospective audits. Where possible they must be based on patients for whom the candidate assumes primary responsibility. It is expected that a completed audit cycle will be demonstrated for each audit. The criteria and standards must be outlined, and a high standard is expected, defined as 90% achievement of the criteria. This area will take considerable time to prepare as a repeat audit is required. To show any significant change in some conditions can often take six months, so it is advisable to make an early start on this section. Although it may not be finished until towards the end of collating your submission, work should be on-going throughout the process.

The remainder parts of area 6 are optional. 6(c) requires description of a recent case of terminal care for which the candidate has had main responsibility, as example 11.5.

Example 11.5   Terminal care

Male age 36 at presentation. Reference 696.

Past medical history

1991	Initial presentation, 12 year h/o intermittent blood PR. Sigmoidoscopy NAD. Rectal biopsy NAD. Sulphasalazine caused bruising.
1992	Haemorrhoids banding
1995	Colitis diagnosed. Treated with symptomatic use of loperamide/codeine phosphate. Not unhappy with his condition.
9/98	Seen by me, in view of a six-year history of colitis with no improvement in condition referred for colonoscopy/large bowel investigations. Blood PR occasionally slime. PR NAD.
11/98	Seen A&E, history of epigastric pain, referred to surgeons.
1/99	Failed to attend for sigmoidoscopy

4/99	Re-wrote to consultant informing of deterioration in condition, increased frequency of bowel actions, now has blood PR.
17/5/99	Home visit, called by wife as his bowel actions had become much more frequent over the previous few weeks. Was due to attend for sigmoidoscopy that afternoon, did not think he could attend. Encouraged to attend, telephoned consultant secretary to inform of patient condition, and that he may need admission
18/5/99	Consultant telephoned, has recto-sigmoid carcinoma.
26/5/99	Anterior-perineal resection. Good recovery although local spread of disease to lymph nodes. District nursing staff attending frequently.
7/99	Pain: Dihydrocodeine 30mg 100. Lactulose prn Nausea: cyclizine 50mg tds prn 100. District nurses and Macmillan nurses informed of the clinical and social circumstances.
7/99	Chemotherapy, reports of regression of liver secondaries.
24/8/99	Seen by me at home, chest infection diagnosed. Cefaclor MR bd for 7 days.
26/8/99	Not really any better, had final chemotherapy two days previously. Change therapy, arranged CXR.
31/8/99	CXR normal, recovering.
2/9/99	Lump noticed in right deltoid, thought to be probably a secondary. Wife given my home telephone number. General condition rapidly deteriorating. Regular home visits, jointly with district nurses.

14/9/99	Starts on morphine as MST and oramorph. District nurses visiting daily. Pain relief discussions with patient and Macmillan nurses. Patient and family aware of situation.
16/9/99	Swelling of left leg, due to pelvic tumour, to see oncologist for palliative radiotherapy.

Rx MST 200mg bd and oramorph 50mg up to qds.

Dies peacefully at 7am next day. Family present. Wife telephones me at home. Follow-up visit two weeks later. Discussion of diagnosis, treatment that was undertaken. Further appointment arranged.

Area 6(d) is similar but for a patient with a chronic debilitating illness. Area 6(e) requires the candidate to have a list of agencies of self-help and support groups.

Such a list may be collated from, among others, the monthly e-mims CDs. Further details of the patients' experiences from the contact are to be described.

7 Patient records

This area has four essential criteria. The first requires that your entries in 20 randomly selected notes will not only be legible but contain sufficient information for another doctor to continue care for that patient. These records can be either paper or electronic. The reception staff may be asked to assist in identifying the candidate's entries. This will be assessed on the visit.

Area 7(b) describes your practice demographics. It is a straightforward one where your practice manager may well help. Area 7(c) is similar, although you may be asked to identify patients with conditions that feature in the management plans in 6(a). Therefore if you are not able personally to produce a list of people with diabetes it is time to learn! Area 7(d) will be assessed at the same time as 7(a). Again either paper or electronic records are acceptable.

8 Practice organisation and team working

This section focuses on the organisational aspects of your working environment and your integration with other medical and paramedical team members. The section has been written to be appropriate if you are a non-principal or assistant.

In 8(a) practice staff will be asked how they deal with incoming calls when you are consulting and how they deal with mail and investigations both when you are present and when you are absent. In 8(b) you are required to describe how you make contact with the people listed. You will be asked to give details of about three of these on the day of assessment. Area 8(c) requires a short description of three case reports in which you have liased with other member of the PHCT. One of these will be discussed on the day of assessment.

A clear practice leaflet will have features such as:

• The names and qualifications of all principals in the practice.
• Surgery times, indicating when appointments are available and when there is an open access session.
• How to contact a doctor in an emergency
• The complaints procedure
• States the clinics which are held and their time and location
• Is current
• Special services available

The two optional areas require a log of relevant contributions to practice team development or personal involvement in organisational/managerial changes. The rationale behind the requirement for change will be described along with the outcome of such changes. An example may be the candidate's role in the selection and appointment of a new member to either employed or attached staff of the PHCT.

9 Prescribing and referral

The final documented section comprises six essential criteria. In 9(a) the discussion will centre on some of the cases presented. It is important to use a recognized source for evidence, which could be *Drugs and Therapeutics* or local information from your PCG/LHG adviser.

Area 9(b), which deals with repeat prescribing, requires that 100 cases are listed with notes of the problem, the medication and the outcome, as shown in the handbook. These must be consecutive, not selected cases. Checks will be made by reference to practice records on some of them to ensure appropriate management. Area 9(c) requires submission of either PACT records or copies of 200 consecutive anonymous prescriptions. Discussion will centre on variability from local norms.

Area 9(d) is concerned with your referral letters. They must be available, therefore keeping a list of your referrals as suggested should be one of the initial planning tasks. It will be necessary to ensure that the letters contain the requisite documentation. In 9(e) some of the previous referrals will be discussed in more detail. Area 9(f) requires a list of local agencies to be developed. This is a very useful file to have if you do not have one already.

The assessment visit

How to apply for a visit is described in detail in the MAP handbook. There will be two assessors, the leader coming from a different RCGP faculty and the other from your own area. A typical plan of a day is shown in table 11.2, page 179.

It should be an enjoyable if somewhat exhausting day for all concerned. The considered report is submitted to the RCGP central offices for ratification, so the assessors are not able to give you the result of the assessment at that time.

Presentation

This needs to be thought of at the beginning. Most applications will be in a loose-leaf file, and it is a requirement that any practice computer printouts that you may wish to use are not inserted as a whole into a plastic cover; each sheet must be presented individually.

The application must be typed, for which many people use a word processing system. Again, the layout is important to plan at an early stage.

General remarks on the presentation

• All references to individual patients should use either initials or, preferably, code numbers

• No patient must be named in the submission

• Any complaints outstanding against you must be notified at the time of submission. The RCGP reserves the right not to elect to membership or Fellowship a doctor who has an unresolved complaint against them

• Paper should be A4, but documents, such as practice leaflets, that are smaller should be in individual clear plastic wallets

• Three copies of the submission are required

• As space will be taken by the hole punch on the left hand side of the paper it may be advisable to increase the margin on the left to 3cm, with 2.5cm on the other three sides

• It is advisable to use double line spacing

• The use of chapter and page numbering, or page numbering alone, can aid discussions on the day of the visit. It may be preferable to use chapter and page numbers because when the inevitable last minute alterations happen the most you have to reprint will be one chapter

• Each chapter needs to start on a new sheet. Numbered dividers help to direct the eye to the start of each chapter

• Fonts: Times New Roman is a conventional typeface, 12 point minimum although alternatives could be styles such as Arial or Century Gothic. It is preferable not to use Courier, as this is a difficult style to follow when reading long sections

Although the assessors will not be judging you on your word-processing ability, all these factors will help the day of the assessment run smoothly — and successfully!

Table 11.2 *Typical visit timetable*	
Task	Time
Assessors plan the outline of the day	60–90 mins
Meet candidate, introductions, tour of practice	20 minutes
First session with candidate	90 minutes
Assessors confer/coffee	20 minutes
Meet staff, review records, check drugs and equipment, emergency and reception procedures	45 minutes
Assessors working separately	60 minutes
Lunch to be taken at appropriate time, meet other practice team members if possible	60 minutes
Final session with candidate	30 minutes
Assessors confer to agree report	

12   After the MRCGP

Richard Moore and Joanna Bircher

New members of the Royal College of General Practitioners can deservedly be pleased with their success in the examination, for it is not easily achieved. The fact that about two thousand candidates choose to sit the examination each year testifies to its acceptability, for doing so, though advantageous, is entirely voluntary.

But success cannot be taken for granted, for one quarter of candidates are unsuccessful. It is not an easy challenge, and it should never be assumed that merely by going through a process of training, or having some experience in practice, will be enough to ensure a pass. Indeed, the introduction of the merit grade in 1998 increases the element of challenge and competition. Previously, when a distinction was the only grade above pass, most candidates would not have considered themselves likely to achieve one, for such recognition was only granted to 40 or 50 of the 2000 doctors who took the exam each year. Now achieving a merit, or better still a distinction, and thereby demonstrating that one is in the top 25-30% of candidates, is an entirely achievable target for many. This incentive to success, and the recognition of greater competence that goes with it, will surely be a great spur to the education of new entrants to the higher levels of the profession.

Another beginning

Success in the MRCGP is the culmination of 10 or more years of study and training for a complex and difficult profession, calling for many varied qualities in its practitioners. Yet passing the examination is only the end of the beginning, for such is the pace of change in the profession today that without further application the knowledge and skills learned with so much hard work will soon need updating. These skills, and the values and attitudes which underlie them must be modified as circumstances change. How then should the new member view the future? How should the education, so laudably undertaken before MRCGP and MAP, continue afterwards? How can education continue in competition with the many other professional and personal demands upon time and energy?

In passing the examination the new member of the College has become eligible to join a professional organisation dedicated to promoting and maintaining high standards in general practice. As David Haslam says in chapter 2, success in MRCGP or MAP is, in fact, the start of real membership of a real College. It is therefore of the greatest importance that those who have qualified for membership should maintain it by remaining subscribing members.

Regrettably there is a tendency to allow subscriptions to lapse when the examination is over, for the College may not appear to have immediate personal or local advantages. It is sad but true that within four years of passing the examination 30% of those who joined the College have left it, and another 4% have not even joined despite their success in the exam. This might be understandable given the pressures on the financial, personal and professional resources of a new entrant to general practice, but only half these erstwhile members resign because of financial pressure. Many say that they believe the subscription does not give value for their money, though what value they expect is unspecified. Ironically, if they had stayed as members the cost of paying for the College's work would be divided among more members and would therefore be less to each member.

To forego membership despite passing the exam is, however, a short-sighted view, for not only does the College need its members and their subscriptions, but the profession of general practice needs a College which can debate the issues of the day with enlightened authority, determine and publicise the quality which it should strive to achieve, and support its members with the necessary research, education and services. These were the objectives which our predecessors in the 19th century dreamed of, and which our founders in the 20th century worked so hard to achieve. We must follow their lead, build on the foundations they have laid and seek that excellence to which a great profession should aspire.

Achievements so far

Seen across the relatively short time since the health service reforms of 1990, it is easy to forget the depth of other crises and changes which the profession has faced since the 1950s. Looking further back over the half-century since it was founded, it is clear that the Royal College of General Practitioners has been a major force in the development of general practice, not only in Britain but throughout the world. It was not medico-political activity which energised this force, but the desire to define the role of the general practitioner and to develop an educational and academic structure which could enable the profession to adapt and develop appropriately. It is this dedication by its membership and the leading individuals within it which has established general practice as both a practical and an academic discipline in its own right within the medical profession. For this reason alone, membership of the College is important. Without members and the necessary funds they subscribe the profession would have no channel through which dedicated people could undertake this work

The College's early years were devoted to acquiring its headquarters and determining policies and, of course, establishing a strong body of membership. The next objective was the development of educational opportunities specifically for general practitioners, and the introduction of general practice as a subject in the undergraduate curriculum, which was then a novel, even revolutionary, idea. It also initiated postgraduate training of doctors to prepare them for general practice, and promoted their continuing education throughout their careers.

Other aims included the enhancement of the esteem with which general practitioners were held by students, specialists and the public, the improvement of the quality and skill of practice by the setting of high standards in parallel with the other royal colleges and the introduction of a diplomas to demonstrate the competence of general practitioners in the broad range of the subjects necessary for practice.

The College has achieved all these aims and more. It has handsome headquarters at Princes Gate, and a faculty structure which makes participation in locally based College activities a practical possibility for all members. The developments in education have been huge, with the foundation of departments of general practice in universities and medical schools and the appointment of deans to oversee the postgraduate programmes in the regions. Above all, the College has led the way in developing the vocational training programme.

These initiatives have enabled the expansion of research, the creation of a body of literature relevant to the needs of general practitioners and the recognition of general practice as a discipline in its own right. Indeed they have met the exact objectives which Dr James Cole and Dr George Ross set out so eloquently in 1844. The College's motto, *Cum Scientia Caritas*, expresses the twin objectives of all general practitioners, to care for our patients and to practise medicine based on scientific principles. The founding steering committee described its idea of a diploma examination as: 'an emblem of quality worth striving for' (Gray, 1992). How does the new member, wearing that emblem and wishing both to be compassionate and to follow scientific principles, maintain and improve the skills and wisdom so necessary for the task that lies ahead, evolving and changing as the years go by?

Opportunities for learning in practice

The introduction of the postgraduate education allowance in 1990 gave a stimulus to educational activity that produced many new ideas, but opportunity is not synonymous with achievement. Mere attendance at a postgraduate event, though measurable, does not guarantee learning. Learning for practising doctors must be largely self-directed, varied according to individual needs, and supported by both the talents of individuals and the collective resources of practices and the profession.

A model for developing a self-directed approach is described by Stanley (Stanley 1993 a & b) consisting of three major sources of learning, which could and should become an everyday part of general practice. Until the end of training and the final tests of summative assessment and MRCGP, the student or junior doctor has often been the object of more-or-less didactic teaching, and the change to self-directed learning at a time of much other change in status and activity needs to be a conscious and deliberate one. The three sources of learning which Stanley describes are all available within the environment of a practice and postgraduate centre. They are:-

• Reading, to provide the firm knowledge base
• Experience, to allow the knowledge acquired to be put in context and used
• Reflection, to enable the knowledge and experience to develop to meet individual circumstances.

Central to all is the concept of audit, not as a contractual requirement directed from outside, but as a means of capturing experience and processing it in order to learn from it. The natural place of learning is the place of work, and in directing his or her learning the individual doctor must select, organise and interpret the experience gained in practice to meet individual needs. This may be done through the opportunities provided by structured postgraduate activities, such as lectures or courses, distance-learning packages and by more or less informal peer group meetings. It may be directed to a specific end such as a diploma, an MSc or MD, for which there are now many opportunities. It may also be achieved by the stimulus of teaching others, by research and writing, or through small-group activities.

Having directed learning where it is required, the doctor will wish to know whether the learning is being properly and appropriately applied; this is where audit plays its part in the educational process. It answers the question: 'Has what I have learned produced improvement in my practice?'. Such audit may be a personal activity or shared with others. In either case, to be meaningful and effective as a method of learning it should originate in the minds of the individual learners, free from external pressures or conditions.

It might seem that on joining a partnership at the age of thirty-something a general practitioner has little in the way of career progress for another 30 years. Indeed, so it used to be, and still can be unless the effort is made to look for challenges and opportunities. Two important features of adult learning are that it should be based on the personal experiences and needs of the learners, and should be generated from their everyday work or activities.

How can a general practitioner, under pressure from the demands of the practice, create such challenges and opportunities? Pietroni described an educational career structure (Pietroni, 1992), the first stages of which are already in place, and the later stages are becoming available now. The early stages are the undergraduate training, pre-registration work and vocational training schemes, leading to the summative assessment procedures and, preferably, the MRCGP examination. Thereafter there are opportunities to study for a doctorate or MSc in relevant subjects and, through continuing education, to Fellowship of the RCGP.

Because these opportunities may necessitate following a curriculum determined by others they may be too prescriptive to meet the needs of individuals, which is why the concept of portfolio-based learning was developed (RCGP 1993). This involves the collection of evidence of learning by an individual, based on his or her needs and interests and consisting of case records, video-recordings, audit and research work and evidence of personal learning. This evidence is then considered with a mentor or supervisor to enhance the learning experience, and could be used as evidence of learning and ability for purposes of revalidation.

A question of quality

The College's objective is the promotion of high-quality care and excellence among its members. One department of the College, its quality network, has specific responsibility for quality, which approaches its task along several lines. It has four main strategies to achieve that quality:

- A methodology for defining clinical standards
- Promotion of opportunities for learning audit skills and activities, in both medical and multi-disciplinary fields

• Development of clinical guidelines and management programmes
• Encouragement to members to work towards fellowship by assessment

The first three of these strategies are examples of how the College takes a lead in developing its educational programme through courses and its journal, occasional papers and various other publications, and by funding research and special fellowships. The fourth is a development unique among medical royal colleges in offering objectives and incentives to individual members to direct their continuing education to their personal needs and apply the benefits derived from it to the improvement of their practices.

Fellowship by assessment

The concept of fellowship by assessment (FBA) may be unfamiliar to those who have recently joined or intend to join the College. It was introduced in 1989, and has already attracted the attention of hundreds of members who have been elected to Fellowship as a result of their endeavours. Members of five or more years standing and in the same practice for two years are eligible to apply. They must prepare a detailed description of their work and the clinical and organisational contributions they have made and intend to make to their practice. This document is then submitted for assessment according to 60 essential criteria, all of which must be met. A videotape of actual consultations by the applicant must also be submitted. Finally, a full-day visit by three assessors to the applicants practice is made.

Essential criteria

The 60 criteria are described as essential, that is they are: 'Criteria below which no Fellow shall fall and the absence of which is, of itself and regardless of other merits, sufficient cause to render the candidate unacceptable' (RCGP, 1990). The candidate must therefore provide documented evidence that all the criteria have been met. This is prepared with the cooperation of a Fellow nominated by the faculty acting a mentor to ensure that the whole range of criteria are adequately covered. No assessment actually takes place until the evidence is complete and of the required standard. On completion of the evidence and formal application, the candidate's practice is visited by a team of three assessors who are all Fellows, of whom one is the candidate's mentor, one is a from the candidate's faculty and one is from another faculty. They check that the criteria are properly fulfilled, inspect the practice, interview the staff, examine drug stocks and equipment, and discuss the videotape and other matters with the candidate. If they are satisfied that all criteria are fulfilled to the necessary standard they recommend that the applicant be elected to Fellowship.

There can be no doubt that the educational challenge of reaching the standard required for fellowship by assessment is a demanding one which will amply reward those who are eager to continue their learning. There is also no doubt that not only the applicant, but the whole practice, benefit from this learning process. An outline of the criteria and the areas assessed are shown in table 12.1 (see page 188).

Thus, commitment to the assessment sets goals to achieve and, because the achievements are to be examined, acts as both guide and stimulus to encourage the candidate to direct his or her own learning. As a long-term target for the new member of the College the prospect of working towards FBA holds many advantages, not least by offering a structure for the developments that must be made and a support system for the difficulties that may be encountered in making them.

If that should seem to be an unreasonably altruistic proposition, it is encouraging to relate that at least one doctor, as soon as he knew that he was successful in the membership examination, set himself the task of preparing for Fellowship intending to achieve it in the minimum time of five years...and did so.

There can be no doubt that the educational challenge of reaching the standard required for FBA is a demanding one which will amply reward those who are eager to continue their learning. It is a long process, often taking two years or even more, to complete the

Figure 12.1   *The areas which are assessed in fellowship by assessment*

Section number

1   Eligibility for FBA
2   Contribution to the practice
           Educational influences and activities
3   Availability for access for routine and urgent matters
4   Continuity of care, with supportive survey
5   The consultation and organisation of care
           Repeat prescribing, visiting rates, referral letters and other correspondence systems
6   Health promotion
           Cervical cytology and immunisation
           Chronic disease management
7   Out-of-hours and emergency care
           Commitment to significant event review with illustrative cases
8   Clinical care
           Early diagnosis, terminal care, 10 disease management protocols and accompanying audits
9   Consultation skills
           Videotape of 10 consultations with structured commentary
10   Resources and their use
11   Prescribing costs and patterns, referral rates, item of service claims and comparisons
           Teamwork
           Primary care team members, nurses and clerical staff
           Written accounts of office systems and procedures
12   Social dimension. The effect of chronic disease on patients lives, and the sources of further help. A list of housebound patients
13   Premises and equipment. Some items are specified
           Reference books
14   Record books and registers
           Preventive health measures, disease register of specified conditions
15   Communication with patients. Practice leaflet
           Patient information about prevention and self-care
16   The future. Plans for development, and evidence of fulfilment of past plans

Further details about fellowship by assessment may be obtained from: The FBA Office, The Vale of Trent Faculty, RCGP, Department of General Practice, The Medical School, Queen's Medical Centre, Nottingham NG4 2 UH.

development necessary to reach the standard required. The quality assurance programme which is implicit in the FBA process can now be said to be demonstrating the very best that can be achieved in general practice, and to be a model for others to follow.

Already it exceeds in the numbers of doctors who have been successful in the other schemes like ISO 9000 (BS 5750) and The King's Fund organizational audit which are much more expensive and do not examine the clinical aspects of practice. It is therefore very likely that not only membership but Fellowship of the College by this form of assessment will become increasingly important in the years ahead.

In this chapter we cannot discuss revalidation in detail, but it is worth remembering that the concept of continuing education for general practice must be seen in the context of the ideas now being debated about the introduction of such a system. Candidates taking the MRCGP examination now are the College of the future. They should plan their continuing education in the knowledge that before long they will face the challenge of revalidation.

They would do well to remain active members of the College, thereby contributing to the debate surrounding its introduction, and influence the form it will take. The College's membership needs to be broadly based and well informed, for only then can the College truly represent the profession in promoting ways to meet its continuing educational needs.

Looking to the future

Through its membership and fellowship assessment systems the Royal College of General Practitioners has defined the high standards that general practitioners should expect to attain. It sets a target that everyone can aim for, and provides logic and reliability in the assessment of outcomes in continuing education for general practitioners. By steadily increasing the number of doctors who are committed to those standards, the College provides a model of good practice throughout the British Isles. New members should take pride in their achievement, and remain active supporters of their College throughout their careers. Such support will be repaid in full measure by the efforts and determination of the College itself to foster the conditions necessary to maintain and improve those standards.

The prologue to this book described the lost opportunities of our predecessors of 150 years ago. How different things might have been if a College like ours had been founded then! The lesson should be learned that the profession of general practice, whatever shape it may take in future, must be moulded by its members acting collectively through a strong and educated organisation. Lest it be thought that this chapter is weighted with demands for an unattainable programme, it will conclude with an epilogue which offers an excellent model to emulate.

Joanna Bircher is the winner of the 1998 Fraser Rose Medal, and in the following paragraphs demonstrates how her commitment to learning will be put into practice in the future. Not everyone can win a medal, of course, but it is feasible, indeed essential, for everyone to rise to the challenges offered by the College and other educational opportunities. Do not hesitate to confront them with ardour and determination!

Epilogue

All candidates who are successful in the MRCGP examination should have come to understand the values which the college represents, and in doing so take the first steps to becoming an active participant in its work. Unfortunately, many talented and competent doctors who pass the exam fail to take up membership, and many others let their membership lapse in the first few years. I intend to continue my involvement, and will certainly try for fellowship by assessment when the time is right. Colleagues ask whether such a plan is worth all the effort and time. There is an easy response to this question: continual involvement with the College provides a well sign-posted path for GPs who strive to deliver the best service to their patients, and make themselves as effective as possible.

Patients feel it is important that their doctor is well trained and continues to keep abreast of change, and it is a matter of personal pride that we do so. In the rapidly changing world of medical advance and consumer expectation it is all too easy to find oneself in 10 years time unable to follow or adapt to the academic challenges of general practice. Revalidation, which is on the horizon, will pick out practitioners who once upon a time were excellent doctors with bright minds, but who after years of neglect now under perform. I suspect it takes years to develop poor practice, just as in the same way as it takes years to develop an excellent one. We all need help to remain good doctors.

MRCGP — preparation for life-long learning

By designing the MRCGP exam to be largely a vocational qualification, and not simply an academic or memory test, the College has done us all a great favour. We have been moulded by a process which gives every candidate the opportunity to develop the skills needed to be a good GP and, more importantly, to maintain this ability. An adult-learning style is central to this. After so many years at medical school and hospital training it is embarrassing to realise that preparation for the MRCGP marks for many our first exposure to the process of self-directed learning.

The fundamental skills needed to be able to look for and correct personal and professional weaknesses can be as foreign to candidates as, say, the skills needed to parachute. However, during the run up to the exam they became as unquestionable as the need to pull the rip cord. It is reassuring to see, with the problem-based learning approach of current medical school education, the young doctors of the future are learning these skills earlier. It was the preparation for the examination rather than winning the award, which gave me the skills and confidence to be able to face a life-long career of personal and professional improvement.

After the exam

Once new MRCGP graduates qualify as GPs and become partners and fully fledged members of the real world, continual improvement takes on a new dimension. In the exam candidates are asked to demonstrate their personal competence and talk about issues where others are involved as observers rather than participants. In the real world there are new, harsher terrains to navigate. Though patients want to know whether their doctor can do a good job clinically they view this within the setting of a wider agenda. They want polite receptionists, good accessibility, phone lines which are not engaged, competent practice nurses and a warm waiting room. They want a fully rounded service of the highest quality. After all, they are unwell and illness is a fearful experience.

At the same time we doctors need to see the people who are the most unwell and help them recover, and stay sane ourselves throughout this difficult task. In the real world, there are so many issues which need to be addressed simultaneously. Maintaining contact with the Royal College of General Practitioners is one way of ensuring you are not alone with this challenge.

The College provides many resources for future professional development. First, it provides a portfolio of activities and structures from which to learn new skills, such as involvement with local faculty boards, education groups, educational systems like PEP on CD-ROM and research networks. Secondly, and probably most importantly, it is full of inspiring people. There are people who have been chasing the elusive excellence, sometimes for decades, and are still running strong and others who have brought about enormous changes in the way we view general practice. There are young principals who face the same challenges together, and are creating and sharing their own solutions. The College gives access to others who have been through similar experiences and have reached different but equally important solutions. If there is an advantage to being awarded the Fraser Rose medal, it is not being asked to contribute to College books, such as this one; it is being given the opportunity to meet with people, who despite important positions and grand titles, still care deeply about patient care.

Reflective learning

Arguably, my success in the exam was as much related to the ability to admit personal failings as demonstrating the skills needed to be a good GP. I have since noted with increasing surprise how patients welcome my honesty regarding uncertain diagnoses alongside the willingness to learn more when they present with a complex problem. This open mind to questions which arise in day-to-day practice, of which I manage to answer less than a third, promotes individual learning. It is the awareness of possible failure that generates a desire to audit my activities. Am I performing as I would like to think I am? Has what I have learned produced improvement in my practice? Audits that arise from a genuine desire to find out how well I'm doing are potent learning tools.

Reflective learning, that which arises from attempting to answer the questions and uncertainties which arise every day, does not have to be a lonely affair. I belong to a small reflective learning group of other young principals. By coincidence rather than design, they are all members of the College. Since they recently passed the exam they are comfortable with the idea of sharing uncertainties, frustrations and concerns.

Here are individuals who are trying to adapt to, and master the same difficulties as myself, and they do so with skill, creativity and compassion. The subject material is as varied as the job we perform. The rewards of being part of this group are immeasurably high and reassuringly practical. Together we can share the job of keeping up to date with the latest evidence and pool knowledge of the more obscure diagnoses and practical issues involved in running a practice.

I can confidently say that my patients have the benefit of a group of GPs from three separate practices working together to improve their care. There is the added bonus of gaining PGEA credits to reflect the learning experience.

If this is the experience locally, I do not doubt that other groups affiliated to the College would be able to offer my patients a similarly good deal. There is the local regional office of the RCGP, the Manchester research and development network and the education network. What will be the benefits to my patients when our practice takes on a GP registrar, student nurses and medical students?

All of these take time and energy, but ultimately by the process of reflection lead to better patient care.

Fellowship by assessment

It is fellowship by assessment of the Royal College of General Practitioners which probably brings the most tangible benefits to a GP's patients. The process of assessment examines the candidate's ability to deliver excellent medicine within the context of the whole practice. As mentioned earlier, care is about the delivery of a fully rounded service. The assessment is an opportunity for any practice to lay itself bare for colleagues to inspect and assess its inner workings.

Candidates for Fellowship obviously have to show they possess the attributes which the College feels reflect its objectives and standards (further the influence and importance of the College). At the same time, however, they have to demonstrate the ability to provide and manage this fully rounded service. If, on the run up to fellowship by assessment, my practice undergoes an improvement as marked as the changes experienced in my own personal skills in the run up to the MRCGP exam, my patients will benefit enormously.

References

Gray DJ, Pereira (1992). History of the Royal College of General Practitioners. *British Journal of General Practice* 42, 29-35.

Pietroni R (1992) New Strategies for higher professional education. *British Journal of General Practice* 42, 294-6.

Royal College of General Practitioners (1990) *Fellowship by Assessment. Occasional Paper 50.* London, RCGP.

Royal College of General Practitioners (1998). *Guide and Criteria for Fellowship by Assessment of the Royal College of General Practitioners.* 9th Version 1998/9. London, RCGP.

Royal College of General Practitioners (1993) *Portfolio-based Learning in General Practice. Occasional Paper 63.* London, RCGP.

Stanley I, Al-Shehri A, Thomas P(1993a) Continuing education for general practice 1. Experience, competence and the media of self-directed learning for general practitioners. *British Journal of General Practice* 43, 210-4.

Stanley I, Al-Shehri A, Thomas P (1993b) Continuing education for general practice 2. Systematic learning from experience. *British Journal of General Practice* 43, 249-53.

Appendix 1
Further reading for chapters 5 and 6

Books

The Doctor's Communication Handbook (2nd edition 1997) Peter Tate. Radcliffe Press.

The Consultation: an Approach to Learning and Teaching (1984) David Pendleton, Theo Schofield, Peter Tate & Peter Havelock. Oxford University Press.

The Inner Consultation (1987) Roger Neighbour. Kluwer Academic Publishers

The Doctor, His Patient and The Illness (1957) Michael Balint. London: Tavistock Publications.

Doctors Talking to Patients (1976) Professor Pat Byrne and Barry Long. RCGP Publications. (Originally London: HMSO)

Meetings Between Experts (1985) David Tuckett, Mary Boulton, Coral Olson and Anthony Williams. Tavistock Publications.

Communicating with Patients (1988) Philip Ley. Croom Helm.

Papers

Waitzkin H and Stoeckle JD (1972) The Communication of Information about Illness. *Advances in Psychosomatic Medicine*, 8,180-215 Karger, Basel.

Marshal Becker et al (1979) Patient perceptions and compliance: recent studies of the health belief model. In *Compliance in Health Care*. Johns Hopkins University Press, Baltimore.

Stott NCH and Davis RH (1979) The Exceptional Potential in each Primary Care Consultation. *Journal of the RCGP*, 29, 201-5.

Greenfield S, Kaplan SH et al (1988) Patients' Participation in Medical Care. *Journal General Internal Medicine*, 88, 448-57.

Savage R and Armstrong D (1990) Effect of a GP's consulting style on patient's satisfaction; a controlled study. *British Medical Journal*, 301, 968-70.

Martin E et al. (1991) 'Why patients consult and what happens when they do.' *British Medical Journal*, 303, 289-92.

Wilson A (1991) Consultation length in general practice: a review. *British Journal of General Practice*, 91, 119-22.

Cromarty I (1996) What do patients think about during their consultations? *British Journal of General Practice* 46, 525-28.

An interesting qualitative study demonstrating that patients routinely consider their relationship with us doctors, and assess if we are in a good mood, are not too tired etc and alter their behaviour accordingly.

Meredith C et al (1996) Information needs of cancer patients in west Scotland. *British Medical Journal* 313, 724-6.★

Benson J and Britten N (1996) Respecting the autonomy of cancer patients when talking with their families. *British Medical Journal* 313, 729-31.★

Ford S, Fallowfield L and Lewis S (1996) Doctor-patient interactions in oncology. *Social Science in Medicine* 42, 11, 1511-1519.★

★These three papers greatly inform the debate about how we do and should talk to seriously ill patients and their relatives.

McDonald IG et al. (1996) Opening Pandora's box: the unpredictability of reassurance by a normal test result. *British Medical Journal* 313, 329-32.

Fitzpatrick R (1996) Telling patients there is nothing wrong. *British Medical Journal* 313, 311.

An excellent leading article in the same issue and on the same theme.

Makoul G, Arnston P and Schofield T (1995) Health promotion in primary care: physician-patient communication and decision making about prescription medications. *Social Science in Medicine* 41, 1241-54.

A detailed study of 271 videorecorded primary care consultations. The authors, two American academics from Chicago and a British GP, highlight major discrepancies between perceived and actual communication, especially in relationship to prescribing. Includes some examples of Dr Peter Tate consulting.

Kai J (1996) a) What worries parents when their pre-school children are acutely ill, and why: a qualitative study. b) Parents' difficulties and information needs in coping with acute illness in pre-school children: a qualitative study. *British Medical Journal* 313, 983-90.

Parents worry about their children and we doctors should find out what worries them and why.

Little P et al. (1997) Open randomised trial of prescribing strategies in managing sore throat. *British Medical Journal* 314, 722-7.

A gem of a paper, highlighting the psychosocial consulting issues relating to prescribing in sore throat.

Appendix 2
A five-minute guide to statistics

Statistics form a small part of critical appraisal. Candidates often do not realise how little they need to know. The range of knowledge is outlined below.

Terminology to be understood

Confidence intervals	Should be narrow Should not contain 0 (zero)
p Values	To be significant, must be <0.05 (ie, 95% certainty result is not reached by chance.
Ideal trials	Appropriate (usually larger) number of subjects Randomised, controlled, double blind
Clinical relevance	Note subjects and setting Compare with your practice
Also need to know	Relative risk (anything <0 means harm rather than benefit) Number needed to treat

Clinical trials

The following system can be used to give a rough check to the statistics of any clinical trial.

The example is a hypothetical trial with 100 treated and 100 control patients.

At a given point in time the results are as follows:-

15 treatment patients have died
20 control patients have died

Further details are given in Table A.

Table A

	OUTCOMES/EVENTS		
	'Positive' (deaths)	'Negative' (alive)	Totals
Treated group	15 'A'	85 'B'	100 =A+B
Control group	20 'C'	80 'D'	100 =C+D
Totals	35 A+C	165 B+D	200

So: Risk reduction on treatment ('Y') =A/(A+B)=15/100=15%
Baseline risk ('X')   =C/(C+D)=20/100=20%

Risk reduction

A useful concept is the 'RRR' (relative risk reduction). This is an expression involving the percentage reduction in events in the treated patients (Y) compared with the controls (X).
In other words: RRR =(1 - Y/X) x 100 =(1 - 15/20) x 100 =25%

Confidence intervals

The true risk reduction can never be known. If the controlled trial is rigorous, the true risk reduction will be somewhere near the trial result. Confidence intervals tell us how close.

Chart 1 shows us the same data appearing from a trial with 100 patients and a trial with 1000 patients. The RRR is the same in each case, 25%.

With 100 patients, the 95% confidence intervals are: -38% to +59%
With 1000 patients, the 95% confidence intervals are: +9% to +41%

• Zero is 'no treatment effect'

• Confidence intervals should not cross RRR = 0 as they do with 100 patient trial. If they do, the trial has not 'proved' statistically that treatment is effective.

• The lower 95% with 1,000 patients is above zero, so the question becomes: 'Is this 9% risk reduction level clinically important?'

• Increasing the sample size sufficiently will make all true differences (however trivial) statistically significant.

• Odds ratio may be used instead of RRR. RRR = zero is equivalent to Log 1 of the odds ratio.

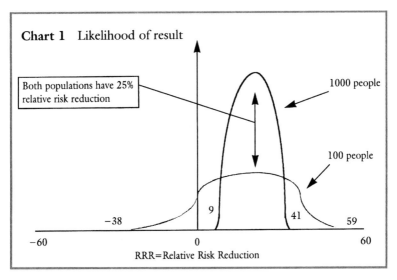

Chart 1   Likelihood of result

Both populations have 25% relative risk reduction

1000 people

100 people

-38

9

41

59

-60

0

60

RRR=Relative Risk Reduction

If there are no confidence intervals reported, then:

• p Value = 0.05 means lower confidence interval lies exactly at 0
Thus if p Value less than 0.05, eg 0.005, it is a significant result

Number needed to treat

Number needed to treat to prevent one event = 1/ (X-Y) x100 = 20

(X = baseline risk, Y = risk on treatment)

Examples: Two patients with recent coronaries

(a) 40-year-old man with a small infarct, normal exercise capacity, no ectopics. Willing to stop smoking, take an aspirin a day, increase exercise, etc.
Risk of death within one year, say, 1%
Beta-blocker would reduce risk by 25%

(b) 60-year-old man, limited exercise capacity, ectopic beats, smokes.
Risk of death within one year, say, 10
Beta-blocker would reduce risk by 25%

The number of patients it would be necessary to treat to prevent one event in each of these two examples is shown in table B.

Table B
EXAMPLE OF NUMBER NEEDED TO TREAT

Baseline risk	Risk on treatment	Relative risk reduction	Number needed to treat
(a) X	Y	(1-Y/X) X 100	1/(X-Y)
1% or 0.01	0.01 X 0.75 = 0.0075	25%	1/0.0025 = 400
(b) 10% or 0.1	0.1 X 0.75 = 0.075	25%	1/0.025 = 40

Next, consider:
Risk to patient if untreated from side effects:
For example, a 10% incidence of fatigue set against saving one life for 400 treated.

Further reading for Chapter 7

Papers

Fowkes FG, Fulton PM (1991) Critical appraisal of published research: introductory guidelines. *British Medical Journal* 302, 1136-40.

Greenhalgh PM (1997) How to read a paper. *British Medical Journal* 315, 243-246.

Oxman AD, Sackett DL., & Guyatt GH (1993) Users' guide to the Medical Literature 1 How to get started *Journal of the American Medical Association* 270, 17, 2093-95.

(First article in an excellent series)

Guyatt GH, Sackett DL, Cook DJ (1994) Users' Guides to Medical Literature. 1 How to use an article about therapy or prevention 2 What were the results and will they help me caring for my patients? *Journal of the American Medical Association* 271, (1) 59-63

Chatellier G, Zapletal E, Lemaitre D, Menard J, Degoulet P (1996) The number needed to treat: a clinically useful nomogram in its proper context. *British Medical Journal* 312, 426-9.

Rothman KJ (1996) Placebo mania: as medical knowledge accumulates, the number of placebo trials should fall. *British Medical Journal* 313, 3-4.

Books

Greenhalgh PM (1998) *How to write a paper. The basics of evidence based medicine.* London: BMJ Publishing Group.

Crombie JK (1996) *The pocket guide to critical appraisal*. London: BMJ Publishing Group.

Jones R (1995) *Critical reading for primary care*. Oxford General Practice series 28. Oxford: Oxford University Press.

Sackett DL (1991) *Clinical Epidemiology: a basic science for clinical medicine*. Boston: Little, Brown.

Clarke R, Croft P (1998) *Critical reading for the reflective practitioner*. Oxford: Butterworth Heineman.

Appendix 3
Text presented to candidates in example question 7.3

Reference: *British Journal of General Practice* 1993, 43, 22

Evaluation of the diagnostic value of pneumatic otoscopy in primary care using the results of tympanometry as a reference standard

R A DE MELKER

SUMMARY. The aim of this study was to determine the value of pneumatic otoscopy in diagnosing otitis media with ef-fusion in primary care. Pneumatic otoscopy was carried out for 111 children aged one to 16 years and the results obtain-ed compared with those obtained from tympanometry. The children were those who had attended for a regular ear, nose and throat check up in the health centre of a school for the deaf during the period November 1989 to January 1990. Pneumatic otoscopy and tympanometry with the GSI 28® instrument (Grason-Stadler) were carried out by a trained ear, nose and throat nurse. All relevant features determined using otoscopy – the colour, position and mobility of the tympanum – and an overall assessment were recorded. The results of tympanometry were evaluated independently of the otoscopic findings. In the population examined the predictive values of positive and negative results of pneumatic otoscopy for diagnosing effusion were high; the sensitivity was low. Serious retraction of the eardrum and absence of mobility under positive pressure were the most predictive features but the colour of the tympanum did not show any relation to effusion. In the youngest age group (one to five years) 56% of the children had abnormal otoscopic findings in either one or both ears (odds rate for this group versus remaining children 3.75; 95% confidence interval (CI) 1.75 to 15.2). The odds ratios of past and present history of upper respiratory tract infection with respect to abnormal results from otoscopy were 2.41 (95% CI 1.05 to 5.63) and 2.95 (95% CI 1.17 to 7.45), respectively.

Pneumatic otoscopy carried out by an experienced health care worker is of high diagnostic value when compared with the results of tympanometry. Pneumatic otoscopy can im-prove the diagnostic capabilities of general practitioners and other primary care workers with regard to otitis media with effusion.

Appendix 4
Text presented to candidates in example question 7.4

Reference: *British Journal of General Practice* 1993, **44**, 370-71

Breast cancer: causes of patients' distress identified by qualitative analysis

R V H JONES

BERNARD GREENWOOD

SUMMARY
Background. *Previous investigations of the psychological consequences of having breast cancer have usually involved quantitative analysis within medical models.*
Aim. *This qualitative study set out to identify key events which had caused distress to women with breast cancer and to compare the frequency of these events with doctors' beliefs about their relative frequency.*
Method. *The causes of distress in 26 women with breast cancer were identified by qualitative analysis of unstructured interviews. Subsequently, all hospital doctors and general practitioners in the Exeter health district were sent a list in random order of the eight events which had most commonly caused distress and were asked to rank them in order of frequency for patients with breast cancer.*
Results. *The responses suggest a mismatch between the doctors' expectations and the experience of the patients.*
Conclusion. *Patients may suffer distress in areas of management doctors do not suspect are important; qualitative analysis can identify these areas.*

Method

Over the period 1988–91 patients with a history of breast cancer from two general practices in Devon were asked by their general practitioner in person to tell the story of their illness to a medical anthropologist (B G) who visited them at home. The interviews were minimally structured. With strict confidentiality safeguards and with the patients' permission each interview was recorded and transcribed on to a word processor. For each patient the situations, actions and events which gave rise to negative and positive emotions were identified by a form of grounded theory.[6,7] The text of each transcribed interview was searched sentence by sentence for words and phrases which indicated negative or positive emotions (markers), for example 'it was just awful', or 'I came home and cried and cried' or 'they explain everything to you — they're marvellous'. The event or aspect of the situation (category) which had given rise to the emotion was then linked to each marker. A list of all the categories identified in the interviews was made and the number of patients in whom each category had occurred was noted.

As a follow up to the identification of causes of distress among patients, all hospital doctors and general practitioners in the Exeter health district were circulated in 1991 with a list containing in random order the eight numerically most frequently reported distressing events as defined in the study. They were asked to rank them in the order of frequency with which they judged them to occur. The overall rankings were calculated separ-ately for the replies received from junior hospital doctors, from hospital specialists and from general practitioners.

Results

Of the 39 women with a history of breast cancer identified six did not wish to be interviewed, seven were considered by their general practitioner to be too ill to be asked, and 26 were interviewed. Eighteen of the 26 women had received radiotherapy; 16 had had a full mastectomy.

Analysis provided 22 spontaneously generated categories, of which 13 had caused distress in five or more women (Table 1).

Accounts of problems following radiotherapy included:

'Your whole personality seems to change. I never had the same energy. Even now most days I have to sleep in the afternoon — for someone of my age that's awful isn't it? It had left me depressed and tired.'

'They didn't warn me about all this. When I went to see them again I was greeted with: "How did you like your Christmas present?" I didn't think that was funny. They never said anything about after effects.'

With regard to prostheses, in addition to problems with the prothesis itself five women reported poor advice and poor service.

'One burst, which wasn't very nice. I went to the doctor and being male he didn't think it was very important, and to me it was the most important think in my life. He didn't understand. I think some older male doctors don't understand.'

'They were horrible then. It used to rise up — it was terrible it really was. It used to be dreadful — that makes you feel bad and it's only this last three years that I've had a decent one. Now it's more natural, like a breast proper.'

'There was only a little shop with a cold back room. They showed you one or two, one of which fitted. They were discussing your breast in the shop with men coming in. I found the thing repulsive.'

From 105 junior hospital doctors 24 completed replies were received, from 62 hospital specialists 18 replies were received and from 100 general practitioners 77 replies were received. The doctors' estimates of the order of frequency of the events causing distress in women is shown in Table 2.

Comparison of Tables 1 and 2 shows that although the first three items on the doctors' list had been distressing events for up to half the women interviewed, a greater proportion of the women had been distressed by the side effects of treatment. The most frequent distressing situation had been depression, weakness and tiredness after radiotherapy. Moreover 13 out of the 16 women who had had a mastectomy had problems with their prosthesis and this was the last or last but one item on the doctors' lists.

The doctor's ranking order which most nearly accorded with the experience related by patients was provided by a junior hospital doctor who added the comment 'Have you considered sorting replies according to whether family members have suffered from this disease? One of mine has.'

Table 1. Causes of distress in women with breast cancer.

Category	No. of patients experiencing distress
All patients (n=26)	
Worry, shock at first symptom	13
Fear of recurrence	12
Being told the diagnosis	11
Problem with doctor (eg attitude, delayed referral)	11
Waiting for appointment at the hospital	9
Radiotherapy treatment (n=18)	
Depressed, weak, tired	15
Burns	12
Sickness	11
Mastectomy (n=16)	
Problems with prosthesis	13
Affected by loss of breast	11
Residual problems with arm	8
Immediate post-operative problems (eg drainage tube)	7
Poor service related to prosthesis	5

n = total number of women in group.

Table 2. Estimate by doctors of order of frequency of causes of distress in women with breast cancer.

	Ranking order of frequency		
Category	Junior hospital doctors (*n* = 24)	Hospital specialists (*n* = 18)	General practitioners (*n* = 77)
Worry, shock at first symptom	1	1	1
Being told the diagnosis	2	2	2
Fear of recurrence	3	3	3
Affected by loss of breast	4	4	4
Depressed, weak, tired after radiotherapy	5	5	5
Sickness with radiotherapy	6	6	6
Problems with prosthesis	7	7	8
Burns with radiotherapy	8	8	7

n = number of respondents in group.

Appendix 5
Further examples of questions
typical of Paper 2 (Chapter 8)

Example A

IRON DEFICIENCY IN INFANCY

1 It is recognized that dietary iron supplementation can safely be administered to children whose iron stores are adequate.

2 Low birth weight is a recognised risk factor.

3 Infants who enjoy prolonged breast feeding are recognized to have a good iron status.

4 Iron-enriched infant formula feeds have been shown to be an effective preventative measure.

5 Clamping of the umbilical cord following cessation of pulsation has been shown to delay depletion of iron stores in late infancy.

6 Afro-Caribbean infants are recognized to have an increased prevalence.

ANSWERS: 1 false,   2 true, 3 true, 4 true, 5 true, 6 true,

Reference to this question *British Medical Journal* 312, 1996,136-7

Example B

A PROBLEM SOLVING MULTIPLE TRUE/FALSE QUESTION

A young man requests an HIV test following casual and unprotected vaginal intercourse two days previously. You can inform him that:

(a) One episode of vaginal intercourse has been shown to transmit HIV

(b) The majority of heterosexuals with HIV have contracted it from abroad

(c) Seroconversion, typically takes up to six months

ANSWERS: a) true   b) true   c) true

Example C

A SINGLE BEST ANSWER QUESTION

Theme: Back pain

Options:

A Ankylosing spondylitis	F Osteomalacia
B Degenerative disc disease	G Osteomyelitis
C Hyperparathyoidism	H Osteoporosis
D Multiple myeloma	I Spinal stenosis
E Myofascial pain	J Spondylolisthesis

Instructions:
For each patient with back pain, select the most likely diagnosis. Each option can be used once, more than once, or not at all. Only one option should be selected for each item.

Items

1 A 30-year-old man was involved in a minor car accident 18 hours ago. He complains of a headache, neck pain and lower back ache. Examination reveals reduced cervical spine movement and tenderness over the lumbar area. Rope-like bands of muscle are present which are painful.

2 A 65-year-old woman complains of pain in her lower back, radiating down both legs when she walks a few yards. The pain disappears when she sits down or squats.

3 A 25-year-old man complains of low back pain. He is not sure how long it has been present. It alternates from side to side. He can experience pain in his buttocks and back of the thighs. He has noticed he feels stiff first thing in the morning and has recently had a red left eye which has not responded to antibiotic eye drops.

ANSWERS: 1 E   2 I   3 A

Appendix 6

Each of these 12 examples of oral questions has been chosen to illustrate one section of the competence-context grid (see chapter 9). Each one shows the examiner's initial question, to which the candidate is invited to respond. As that response develops the examiner may pose other questions to take the discussion further without moving away from the original context (eg those marked ★★ in examples 1, 2, 3, 5, 9 and 11). Readers are encouraged to develop suitable answers and discuss the issues they raise with colleagues.

Area of competence — communication

1 Context — care of the patient:

> *What strategies do you have to discuss child abuse with a potential abuser?'*
> ★★ *'How would you decide which strategy to use?'*

2 Context — working with colleagues:

> *'What strategies do you have for communicating with a practice team?'*
> ★★ *'How would you decide when to bring in an outside facilitator?'*

3 Context — society:

> *'Problems arising from access to the Internet and increasing patient expectations may be best met by a patient centred consultation. How do you decide whether to adopt a patient or doctor centred approach?'*

★★'*Is there any disadvantage to being patient centred all the time?*'

4 Context — Personal growth:

'*How do you personally know whether your own consultation skills are good or not?*'

Area of competence — professional values

5 Context— care of the patient:

'*What are the pros and cons of using a chaperone?*'
★★'*How would you decide when to use a chaperone?*'

6 Context — working with colleagues:

'*A locum doctor arrives smelling of alcohol. How would you decide what to do?*'

7 Context — society:

'*Families appear to be becoming de-skilled at handling minor illness. Should we decide to tackle this problem and, if so, how?*'

8 Context — personal growth:

'*How do you personally decide to use a new drug or not?*'

Area of competence — personal and professional growth

9 Context — care of the patient:

'*In what situations do you personally feel uncomfortable with a patient?*'
★★'*How would you decide when to confront a patient?*'

10 Context — working with colleagues:

'*You are asked to give a talk to final year undergraduates about your own work in primary care. How would you decide what to include in your talk?*'

11 Context — society:

'*Do you believe society should be protected from an under-performing GP?*'
** *How would you structure your own career to avoid being in such a situation?*'

12 Context — personal growth:

'*What strategies might you use to keep yourself up to date?*'

Index

summative assessment, 13-14, 26, 29,
    74, 80
- compulsory, 19
- exemption, 19
- system, regional advisers', viii
- MCQ, 14-15
supporting the discipline, xvi-xvii
Swanson, Dr David, 8

Tate, Peter, ix
team, 12, 38
- member, 55
- working, 166, 176
technique, points of, 135-6
theoretical knowledge, 99-102
thinking
- lateral 100
- systematic, 99
time, 48-49, 86
timing, 94
trainers report, 14
training, 19, 25, 27

Update, 103
Users' Guide to the Medical Literature,
    105

validity, 31
values
- attitudes, 38
- predictive, 99
video, 12
- assessment of consulting skills, 14,
    27, 58-82
    - results of, 81
- preparing, 73-6
- workbook, 166

vocational
- training, xiii
    - Act, xvii

workbook, 58, 63, 70, 73
- completing the, 78-80
working diagnosis, 68, 70, 78
written
- examination, 18, 27, 96-119
- material, evaluate and interpret, 98-9
- papers, 35
    - question design, 96-102
    - preparation for, 102-19
- work, 14